MANAGING QUALITY DYNAMICS

MANAGING
QUALITY DYNAMICS

·

JAMES TEBOUL

Prentice Hall
New York   London   Toronto   Sydney   Singapore

First published 1991 by
Prentice Hall International (UK) Ltd
66 Wood Lane End, Hemel Hempstead
Hertfordshire HP2 4RG
A division of
Simon & Schuster International Group

Typeset in 10/12½ pt Times
by MCS Ltd, Salisbury

Printed and bound in Great Britain by
Dotesios Ltd, Trowbridge, Wiltshire.

Library of Congress Cataloging-in-Publication Data is available from the publisher

British Library Cataloguing-in-Publication Data

Teboul, James
  Managing quality dynamics.
  I. Title
  658.5

  ISBN 0-13-553462-3

1 2 3 4 5   95 94 93 92 91

To Jean Claude Hachette

CONTENTS

CONTENTS

FOREWORD

Why another book on quality, when so many papers and articles on the subject already exist? It is precisely this proliferation, together with the constant call by consultants for a revolution in the art of management which has prompted me to attempt a synthesis, and to prepare an orientation map which helps to position the total quality movement within traditional company management. I prefer to use the term reform rather than revolution, since the need is to enhance and deepen the existing management disciplines.

First of all, it seemed to me essential to start with a definition of the word 'quality', since its original operational significance inside the organization was low-key, at the level of control and inspection. It has since grown away from this precise sense, ballooning out to cover all aspects. I have, therefore, used the image showing the squaring of the circle to demonstrate how the present concept linked marketing to production, and was integrated into the strategy of the organization. Like certain other writers, I could have used the term 'excellence' or 'progress', combined with an adjective like 'competitive' or 'strategic'. For the sake of economy, I have stuck to the word 'quality', but at no moment should the reader lose sight of the dual and dynamic aspect of this concept.

So, what does this revolution, or reform, consist of? In an environment which is becoming more and more competitive and complex, the need to differentiate not only pushes quality to the forefront of production missions, but also necessitates an ever more rapid and competitive response to customer requirements, which must be communicated as directly as possible to all departments, services and work areas.

Because the concept of quality needs a qualifying adjective to make sense, I have chosen the word 'dynamics' rather than total, because every manager owes it to himself to better understand, control and improve the processes and systems for which he is responsible, by gaining a deeper insight and achieving a permanent adjustment which goes beyond the necessary reorganization and innovation.

The quality dynamic also encompasses the Juran concept of breakthrough for continuous improvement, Deming's PDCA wheel (Plan, Do, Check, Act) and the Japanese Kaizen system described by Imai in his book. With this concept we are, therefore, leaving behind the operational level of quality control or quality assurance to function right away at the level of the management of the organization.

Management *by* objectives is no longer sufficient, since results expressed in volume or turnover remain abstract, and only relate indirectly to the creative process. In order to maintain, and even improve, performance at all levels, it is essential to proceed to a management *for* objectives. This means returning to the actual and concrete processes, in order to understand, control and improve them. It also becomes essential to introduce method and intelligence to analyze how organizations and technical systems function and change, to install visible measurements and physical audits, to break down barriers and help to re-establish co-operation.

In order to have a general perspective, I have selected two lines of observation. Organizations take into account the strategic importance of quality by working from the inside out. The quality reform starts with the physical, operational and economic aspects of the organization. This is the first economic and social reform described in Chapters 4, 5 and 6. In Chapter 7 the second reform establishes quality as a strategic weapon.

This evolution from internal strengthening to external affirmation forms the first line of observation. The second shows two interlocking levels of observation; at the bottom, the elementary processes and above that, the system and the organization considered as a whole. Quality dynamics therefore combine the integration of different elements in a long-term strategic plan, and the necessary decentralization to facilitate continuous improvement.

Service industries are becoming ever more predominant and so it was important to explain how the above concept could still be applied. Chapter 8 gives the operational definition of a service delivery system. In Chapter 9, I show the specificity of quality dynamics in services throughout the organization.

Chapter 10 then explains how to implement this change process throughout the organization. I have not given much space in this book to the description of tools, as many good books on this subject already exist. On the other hand, it seemed useful to provide in Chapter 11 an orientation map to situate the different tools available, and to demonstrate how scientific method differs from an empirical approach for solving problems.

The abundance of diagrams should not hide my constant concern to reduce, as much as possible, the number of different symbols. I think that managers and people of action visualize rather than conceptualize situations, and it is the difference discerned in their perceptual maps which make them react. Images and diagrams help people to memorize concepts and facilitate their application to a concrete situation. The definition of quality as squaring the circle, and the pump analogy to describe the implementation of the change process, are images which may seem somewhat mechanical but which are reasonably condensed, economical and easy to memorize.

This book has greatly benefited from questions, discussions and contributions from participants in seminars at INSEAD, CEDEP, and in companies too numerous to list here.

Many companies, in particular Renault and Valeo, have made me very welcome and I would like to thank them. I would particularly like to mention Mr Michel Caillault, Director of Peugeot, Madrid, whose experience has greatly helped me, as well as Roger M. Wymme, from the University of Bradford for his helpful suggestions. I would like to thank Charlotte Butler for her editorial assistance and Nathalie Cornu for her patience in typing and retyping the manuscript. Finally, this work could not have been completed without the help of INSEAD and CEDEP.

PART I

•

HISTORY AND DEFINITION OF QUALITY

The first two chapters explain how and why the total quality movement became so essential, and provide an operational definition of the term.

Chapter 1: The importance of the quality dimension

Chapter 2: The definition of quality

CHAPTER 1

•

THE IMPORTANCE OF THE QUALITY
DIMENSION

1.1 TOWARDS A NEW QUALITY APPROACH

Quality was once a little known or understood part of the production process, banished to the underworld known as the shop floor and ignored by all but a few managers. During the last few years, however, a dawning realization of its importance has caused this hitherto neglected dimension to emerge from the darkness. Slowly, it has inched its way up through the ranks of the firm until today it has emerged into the full light as a major preoccupation in board rooms and executive committee rooms throughout Europe and the United States. This metamorphosis is no accident but part of a broader movement, namely the rediscovery of the importance of production and the management of operations as a means of differentiating the corporation and triumphing over the competition. For many years the production function was enclosed by a one-dimensional logic of cost cutting and productivity gains, governed by the attitude that the less it was talked about the better. Once this strait-jacket burst open, the production function, whether industrial or service, could no longer be ignored or relegated to a back seat behind marketing or finance.

All companies rely physically on the quality of their work-force, their know-how and their production systems. What has not been sufficiently understood until recently is that the patient, continuing improvement of these elements, through internal mobilization and an offensive external policy, can be the means of generating decisive competitive advantages.

However, this can only be achieved by jettisoning a number of passive views, and abandoning the fatalistic approach which submissively accepts poorly controlled inventories and flows, the notion of an acceptable defect or breakdown level, or the inevitability of last-minute engineering changeovers for a new product. Delays, crises, time lags, unduly long information processing cycles: for too long and too often businesses have resigned themselves to managing the inevitable as best they could and accepting such things as a necessary evil, inherent both in the system and the human factor. As long as this view of the production function holds sway, decisive improvement is, of course, impossible. To achieve meaningful progress, managers must replace this negative approach by a radical new vision, one that will offer them an exciting challenge on new terms.

The first step must be to reverse these paradigms and inevitabilities, and instead aim at zero defects, zero breakdown, zero inventory, zero delay, zero paper – all without increasing costs; in fact if anything, by reducing them. In addition to this internal challenge, however, there is also an external one: to create a new, all-embracing dynamism that will transform the solution to a problem into an opportunity. Quality, delivery, flexibility – all these can become formidable weapons for the creating of decisive strategic advantages in outside markets.

In order to rediscover these dimensions which, under pressure of short-term necessity have either been lost sight of or totally forgotten, the corporation must become more concrete. Is this just wishful thinking? Not at all. However, quality, conformity, compliance with schedules, just-in-time, cost control and flexibility cannot merely be decreed from above, but must be built up step by step, within the context of a long-term vision that is backed by solid determination.

This book will focus on the quality dimension, since this lies at the root of the current challenge, beginning with an analysis of the reasons for its development and urgency. A brief historical recap will bring out other structural pointers to the movement towards total quality.

1.2 WHY QUALITY?

1.2.1 The Intensification of International Competition in Industry and the Services

While by no means a new phenomenon, the gradual disappearance of regional or national markets has added a new dimension to competition which Western firms have been slow to comprehend. Additionally, as more countries acquire the capability to produce and export sophisticated goods with cheaper labour costs, business is becoming increasingly international, and this globalization of competition may eventually lead to the disappearance of traditionally acquired markets. The French automobile industry, for example, is still paying for the explosion of a long-held fallacy: that the French market was a protected one. In this field, the 'Toyota syndrome' illustrates a more general phenomenon: our era of communications has transformed the customer into a free subject who travels, makes comparisons, changes his or her mind, and is capable of adapting to a product offered by a global corporation. This product, which can be sold throughout the world at a lower price, is of impeccable quality.

As competition opens up, customers (and we are all customers) can and will become increasingly demanding. As a result, the usual concepts of performance, costs and economies of scale will no longer be sufficient to help determine customer strategy, and it will be essential to differentiate the product by offering a distinct, unquestionable advantage. Quality can provide the source of this essential difference. The challenge is enormous: how to combine mass production with quality, and make this a standard requirement.

Quality has been identified as the very core of the Japanese commercial offensive. Japanese firms, which entered foreign markets discreetly in the 1960s, were perceived as a serious threat in the 1970s due to a determined but not particularly imaginative strategy based on quality, reliability and low costs. Initially, the threat was limited to conventional consumer products such as televisions, cameras, watches, videos, hi-fis and electronic components. However, in the 1980s this trend became increasingly generalized to cover automobiles, computers and fine chemistry, and then international trade and financial services. The Japanese success story demonstrated that when attempting to create a decisive difference, the importance of quality and production know-how as strategic weapons could no longer be ignored.

However, for a long while these lessons were lost on many Western corporations, and they have only just begun, or are about to begin, the attempt to catch up. Others, by contrast, quickly realized that there was only one way to take up the quality challenge, and that was by taking the offensive. In the early 1980s Xerox, for example, noted that the cost price of some of their photocopying machines was the same as the sale price of their Japanese equivalent which was being sold in France, and that they were also at a disadvantage as far as quality and reliability were concerned. It took them five or six years to turn the situation round, but they eventually made it and in November 1989 they received the Baldrige US national quality award. (For more explanations refer to Chapter 10 and Table 10.2.)

1.2.2 Acceleration of Innovation

Another effect of increased competitive pressure is the multiplication of the number of products and services offered, while at the same time the duration of their life cycle is reduced. (In Figure 1.1 it is possible to imagine the influence of life-cycle reduction on the cash flow.) Half the goods produced by Philips, for example, have a commercial life span of less than three years.

The parallel reduction of the development cycle has made necessary an even more methodical and systemic organization of quality. A company can no longer afford to be late with a new product (influence on cash flow can be seen in Figure 1.1) or to market mediocre products and give these 'lemons' to early customers, and then gradually improve the quality as time goes by.

1.2.3 Increasing Complexity

Today's products and services not only use increasingly sophisticated technologies and processes, they are also becoming more complex in themselves. The variety offered is sometimes so wide that it is virtually impossible to forecast the many options that will be produced over a short period.

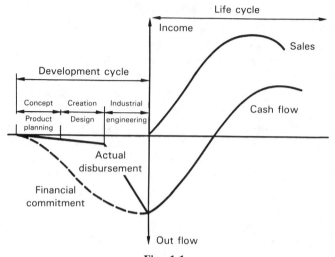

Fig. 1.1

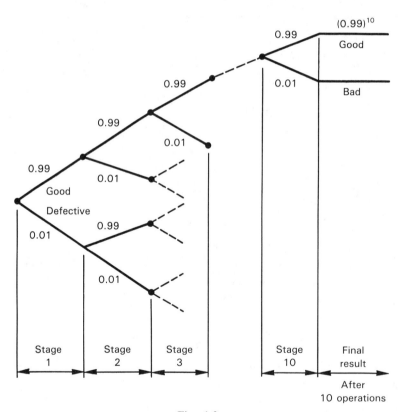

Fig. 1.2

As long as products and services were relatively simple and standard, it was possible to tolerate a non-quality level of around 1 per cent in the inspection of raw materials and finished products. In fact, for many years Western industrial culture was based on a 1 per cent average level of defect when using statistical sampling plans to inspect manufactured batches. Statistical sampling plans (of the military standard type) were incapable of filtering out defects beyond a level between 0.5 per cent and 1 per cent. Thus when the procurement contract for a component prescribed the use of sampling plans based on current standards, the client was forced to accept a defect level of around 1 per cent.

Figure 1.2 is an example of an invoicing process involving ten successive, independent stages. The first operation at stage 1 is good with a probability of 0.99 and defective with a probability of 0.01. The second operation at stage 2 is good with a probability of 0.99 and defective with a probability of 0.01, and so on. The invoice is only satisfactory if all the operations are correctly carried out. Only 'good' branches are acceptable. The probability of this being the case is obtained by the product of the probabilities along the top path (if all operations are independent):

$$\text{Probability of a good invoice} = (0.99)^{10} = 0.91$$

This means a defect level of approximately 10 per cent, i.e. one invoice in ten will be wrong, which is bad news for the customer.

Now consider a fairly simple product comprising fifty parts or components. Based on the 1 per cent culture, i.e. considering that each component has a 1 per cent probability of being defective, we obtain:

$$\text{Probability of a good machine} = (0.99)^{50} = 0.60$$

i.e. Forty machines out of one hundred will have to be reworked. A very costly process!

As a final example, take a television set or a car where the number of components ranges from 500 to several thousands. For simplicity, let us say 1,000 components:

$$\text{Probability of a good unit} = (0.99)^{1000} = 0.00004$$

i.e. Forty chances in every million to get a car without a single defect. Almost a miracle! In this case, each car will have an average:

$$np = 1000 \times 0.01 = 10 \text{ defects/unit.}^{*}$$

The 1 per cent culture can thus lead to significant inspection and rework costs. Moreover, the solution does not lie in merely reducing the defect rate, as the

---

* According to the binomial law, if $n = 1000$ parts and $p = 0.01$ the average number of defects per unit is $np = 10$. If $n = 1000$ and $p = 0.001$, the average number of defects per unit is $np = 1$. In the automobile industry the 'things gone wrong' indicator measuring the average number of problems on a car during the first year of warranty has gradually decreased from 5 to 2 for Western car manufacturers between 1980 and the present.

calculations below clearly demonstrate. One defect per thousand gives the following results:

$$(0.999)^{50} = 0.95$$
$$(0.999)^{1000} = 0.37$$

This is better, but still not adequate. In fact, the only way of obliterating the logic of failure is to aim directly for zero defect, zero error:

$$1^{50} = 1$$
$$1^{1000} = 1$$

The radical nature of this change of vision is highlighted by a change of scale. If we measure in parts per million:

Instead of 1 per cent we then have 10 000 ppm.

One defect in a hundred corresponds to 10 000 defects in 1 000 000 parts.

Under a microscope magnifying 10 000 times, error rates appear enormous and clearly show the need for change. The shock of this realization provides a beneficial lesson. Non-quality becomes totally unacceptable. Table 1.1 shows the history of component quality levels at IBM between 1980 and 1985. Translated to the percentage scale, the quality level of the components during this period gives the results shown in Table 1.2.

Corporate directors and management are not the only ones paying more and more attention to the ill effects of non-quality. Customers are also having their say.

1.2.4 Customer Sensitivity to Risk

The product or service purchased by a customer is unique and must correspond to the promises made. The client is not interested in statistics; what he or she wants is the product or service as promised. No trouble, no risk. However, in the 1 per cent defect culture it is extremely difficult to eliminate major risk entirely, even with the inspection of every single unit and the best will in the world. In any case, the cost of 100 per cent inspection soon becomes prohibitive, in addition to being only 85 per cent efficient (when manual and not automated).

At the same time, customers are becoming less reluctant to file proceedings against a firm which has failed to keep its promises, and nowadays frequently claim substantial damages. The rocketing number of lawsuits for medical malpractice being brought in the US courts is a matter of serious concern to US practitioners, and highlights the acuteness and extent of this new development. Consumer associations are obtaining the recall of insufficiently tested products. In 1978, for example, Firestone was forced to recall certain radial carcass tyres. When the matter was finally settled, the bill was close to 200 million dollars. While the backlash was serious, it did have the advantage of stressing this crucial issue.

In this environment, the only way to satisfy increasingly sensitive and informed

Table 1.1

	1980	1985
	Figures in ppm	
Transistors	2800	80
Micro-processors	4800	400
Transformers	4200	50
Resistors	1200	20

Source: W. Eggleston, Vice President, Quality, IBM. Proceedings of the 4th Annual Operations Management Association Meeting, Tempe, AZ, 1985.

Table 1.2

	1980	1985
Transistors	0.28%	0.008%
Micro-processors	0.48%	0.040%
Transformers	0.42%	0.005%
Resistors	0.12%	0.002%

Source: As for Table 1.1.

customers is to adopt an uncompromising policy of doing the job right first time. This means building quality into the product or service from the outset.

1.2.5 More and More

In an increasingly open and competitive market, customers look for ways of distinguishing between offers. As products become increasingly standardized, companies must find new ways of differentiating them, which means the products must be continuously upgraded. After performance, conformity and reliability follows better service, shorter lead times, or a lower overall life-cycle cost. (Life-cycle cost, or cost of ownership, is the sum of all costs involved in using a product from purchase to destruction – acquisition cost, logistics costs, operating costs, maintenance and service costs.)

In the race to improve market share and increase customer loyalty it is quality, even more so than price, that can be the key differentiating factor. The question is, at what price?

1.2.6 The Non-quality Gold Mine

The fallacy that quality is expensive is solidly embedded in the culture of Western corporations. It is linked to a product perception: a sophisticated product costs more than a simple one. But this prejudice is no longer valid if we consider the production and delivery process and measure the cost of quality, which is obtained by adding the cost of prevention, the cost of inspection or appraisal, the cost of internal failures and the cost of warranties. These costs add up to a fantastic gold mine of 20 per cent to 30 per cent of a company's revenue. This figure is mainly the result of hidden costs and non-added value due to multiple tests and inspection, modifications, rework and rejects, losses of capacity, stocks, irregular production, returns, claims, crises... This 20 per cent to 30 per cent of total revenue represents not just a nightmare but a 'hidden factory', existing solely to manufacture defects and non-values, to produce variability and errors.

The existence of this hidden factory has been uncovered by numerous corporations, much to their surprise. The exact figure, be it 20 per cent or 30 per cent of revenue, is not important. The point is that it is substantial enough to stagger CEOs and consultants. The question then is, how to reach this hidden, unattainable 'deposit', which embraces the entire corporation but is rather more concentrated at the interfaces between services and departments?

As must be patently clear by now, the answer is to be found in a radical change of direction and vision by the company to place the quality dimension at its heart. Quality is not just a strategic weapon for increasing market share, it can also lead to cost reduction and productivity gains.

This entails the complete reversal of a preconceived idea; quality is not a problem but a solution: a solution to the permanent need to reduce costs and become more competitive.

1.2.7 Cultural Change and Better Use of Human Resources

Competitive positioning, or exploiting the full potential of the elimination of non-value or non-quality, requires a methodology, discipline and above all the mobilization of the entire work-force to clarify the objectives, to get the job done right first time and to anticipate problems. By handing over responsibility for quality control, improvement, maintenance, planning and prevention to its employees, and by breaking down the barriers between departments and services, the corporation is going beyond a simplistic Taylorian approach. By doing so, it is beginning to move towards more know-how and professionalism and less hierarchy; in a nutshell, towards different modes of leadership and motivation.

Quality can thus be used to unite efforts with the aim of changing a corporate culture. The values underlying action and change are not external and abstract, but are gradually built up through the daily practice of improvement, problem solving and learning. As a result, quality concepts become the backcloth to training and education. In addition, quality can help build a common language for different trades in order to build co-operation. As Kaoru Ishikawa observed, quality begins and ends with education. A firm which improves its quality not only learns but learns to learn.

Quality has a long history, though to us it is a recent phenomenon. The process of understanding the concept has already gone through several phases, and management may well find that, between an awareness of quality as a problem and an understanding of it as a dynamic solution, it has accomplished the equivalent of a Copernican revolution. Briefly outlined, these phases are as follows.

1.3   FROM QUALITY CONTROL TO QUALITY DYNAMICS IN THE WEST

1.3.1   The Beginnings of Quality Control

Quality control came about when the mass production of the components of a product, and their assembly on the line, led to the need to produce standard, interchangeable parts.

When a craftsman made an object such as a piece of furniture for a given customer, he adjusted one part to another without any undue concern for standardization. The customer was close at hand, able to judge the final quality and possibly suggest improvements. The industrial revolution and mass production, however, channelled industry into a one-dimensional logic based on the division of labour and productivity gains: greater production with a few specialized workers. Taylorism, time and motion study and the scientific organization of work meant that large production centres were set up remote from the market. As products became standardized to allow for mass production, quality control was the answer to the need to ensure the interchangeability of parts produced in large batches.

The race to reduce costs by economies of scale led to the fatal separation of workers or operators from their colleagues in design, method and planning. In this situation how could the workers, who were mere operators assessed solely on the basis of quantity and yield, be responsible for controlling their own quality? At first this was made the supervisor's responsibility, but in the conflict between productivity and quality, he or she was both judge and jury. The quality control department was born to resolve this dilemma. It used specific tools, measuring instruments and increasingly sophisticated statistical methods, and as time went on enlarged the scope of its responsibilities.

During the 1930s, statistical sampling methods were developed to cope with increasing volumes. In the Bell Telephone laboratories, Shewart developed production process control methods using charts to monitor on-line the mean and the range of certain critical parameters. Dodge and Romig developed acceptance sampling plans based on average outgoing quality, in which batches received were inspected using the sampling plan, and rejected batches sorted to remove defective components.

As is frequently the case, war accelerated change. Acceptance sampling was fully developed under the impetus of the US army demands in the 1940s. The so-called military standard procedures codified a method which gradually spread first throughout the rest of US industry, and then on to Europe. Military standards are based on the Average Quality Limit (AQL), meaning the maximum per cent defective that can be considered satisfactory as an average of the quality presented. Industry was thus entering the 1 per cent defect culture, since this method does not enable filtering beyond 1 per cent (with a reasonable sample size).

In the 1950s the development and increased sophistication of the electronic equipment used by the armed forces (soon to be followed by the space agencies) posed an additional problem. Operational and maintenance costs grew bigger than the purchasing price, and the mean time between failures (MTBF) of some radars could be ridiculously short (in the order of a few hours). Thus, towards the end of the 1950s a new discipline was born: reliability. This studies the probability that a device will carry out the required function under given service conditions for a given period of time.

The quality control department then adopted the structure shown in Figure 1.3. It should be noted that the head of the quality department had increased responsibilities, was sometimes at the same level as production or marketing, and joined the executive committee. Nevertheless, quality aroused little interest inside the corporation, where it continued to be perceived as a necessary evil; a parasitic tax, the cost of which had to be reduced.

Despite pre-inspection levels which would sound horrific by today's standards (a defect rate of between 15 per cent and 30 per cent on internal manufacturing processes), the level of final quality reached after inspection was about 1 per cent. Given the limits of the sampling methods used, and the trade-off between the inspection or appraisal cost (which would rapidly become prohibitive if one attempted to be exhaustive and inspect unit by unit) and the failure cost acceptable to the customer, the quality level finally achieved could not be any better than 1 per cent. (See Figure 1.4.) The trade-off prevented the Western world from abandoning 'this vision', the culture of a 1 per cent defect level. Poor quality, it was concluded, had to be accepted and managed.

Naturally, when the defect was critical, 100 per cent inspection methods were

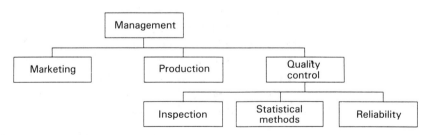

Fig. 1.3

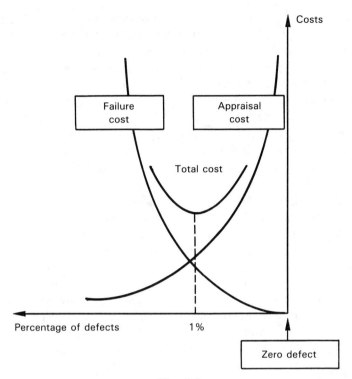

Fig. 1.4

required. However, unless unit by unit inspection is automated it cannot be 100 per cent reliable, and a second inspection may be required.

Ultimately, the 1 per cent level was tolerable inasmuch as it corresponded to the norm for the entire industry. The corollary was that industry as a whole adopted a defensive attitude, perfectly illustrated by the very term 'quality assurance'. However, this cautious approach did not last for long. More aggressive competitors soon loomed on the horizon.

1.3.2 Quality Assurance and Total Quality Control

During the 1960s, an awareness of the increasing cost of the quality control department led to a change of attitude. In its attempts to assume and ensure a sufficient level of protection in sensitive industries such as aeronautics, aerospace or the nuclear industry, the importance of the quality control (QC) department was growing dramatically. Feigenbaum provided an initial response to this development in his book entitled *Total Quality Control*, published during that period.

He argued that to get away from the previous dilemma of 'appraisal versus failure cost' a third term must be introduced: prevention. Since inspection always came too late, and in most cases merely confirmed the death of the patient, quality must be built in from the outset. Prevention, as always, was better than cure. Juran had already reached a similar conclusion. He had introduced the quality spiral, which explained how every department was involved in final quality. The contribution of Deming, a fervent defender of statistical process control at each process level should also be mentioned here.

The quality department was the first to undertake the prevention mission by co-ordinating quality assurance at each stage. It took on a new title, the 'quality assurance department', and set up methods, systems, procedures (often expensive and cumbersome) to try and make the whole system foolproof. At this time, the structure of the quality department resembled the chart shown in Figure 1.5.

While this new setup had its faults, it did represent undeniable progress: quality assurance was attempting to act in co-operation with the various design and production processes. From this time on, prevention was to prevail over inspection.

Although the quality assurance department was now playing an essential role in co-ordination and foolproofing, the fact that it was obliged to confine itself to an auditing role still left it in a somewhat ambiguous position. Any attempt to go beyond this role risked arousing antagonism between doers and controllers, and ending in deadlock. Clearly, a decisive turnaround can only occur if or when management becomes aware of its quality responsibility. This responsibility is the specific domain of management and can never be delegated to a specialized department. To paraphrase Clemenceau, like war, it is too important to be entrusted to specialists alone.

This conclusion then raised the question of how to convince management of this responsibility. The answer was by highlighting a key aspect dear to their hearts: the language of money (Juran) rather than the language of things and techniques. In other words, by demonstrating that better quality reduced costs and increased productivity.

In fact Deming, the champion of statistical process control since the 1940s, had always rejected the theory of mass inspection, and maintained from the outset that quality was the direct responsibility of the producers themselves. It was their job,

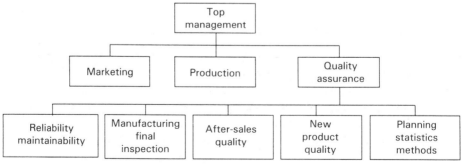

Fig. 1.5

he argued, to dispel the fog surrounding and concealing their processes, and therefore managers should be made responsible for the control and improvement of those processes. Thirty years later, Deming's message became even more direct: 'the basic cause of sickness in American industry and resulting unemployment is the failure of top management to manage' (1982, 1986, preface).

Very early on, Juran also recognized the essential role of management in bringing about continued quality improvement. He proposed improvement on a project by project basis, using a systematic experimental method going from symptoms to causes, from causes to solutions and from solutions to new practices and their consolidation. Every director, every manager should undertake such improvement projects and fit them into an overall plan. Initially, the cost of poor quality would be used as a guide for project selection. The richest seams of the non-quality mine would be tackled first, in line with the Pareto principle which Juran helped to popularize; first deal with the few vital problems, then tackle the more numerous, trivial problems later.

However, these messages only began to reach the Western world in the 1970s and 1980s. Their importance and their audience increased as the Japanese success story became more widespread.

But to return to our historical survey; in the 1960s one company, the Martin corporation which was building Pershing missiles, refused to bow to the apparently inevitable. As early as 1961, thanks to a new awareness and change of attitude on the part of its management, and with a co-operative effort from the entire work-force, it succeeded in manufacturing an operating missile right the first time. It was the dawn of the zero defect movement. This is based on a radical change of attitude, combined with the mobilization of personnel, towards the only acceptable standard: zero defect.

Inspired by this experiment Philip Crosby, then a Martin employee, built his own quality approach based on zero defect programmes. To get it right first time, he stipulated, prevention must be organized and attitudes have to change. The effect of this was to add a third term, hitherto ignored, to the first trade-off (appraisal cost versus failure cost). The third term was prevention cost. Figure 1.6 represents this evolution from stage 2 to stage 3.

The cost ratio between a defect avoided by eliminating a bad component before manufacture, and a defect discovered on final inspection, can easily reach 1000. Between an error avoided when drafting a document or writing a line of software and an error found in the field when using the printed document or the final software package, the cost ratio can be even greater. Investing in prevention is, therefore, extremely profitable. This is a simple straightforward demonstration of the fact that 'quality is free', to use the title of Philip Crosby's book published in 1980.

Thus, by saying to the CEO: 'the cost of quality is 20 per cent of your revenue and I can help you halve it over a five-year period', Crosby was sure of getting his

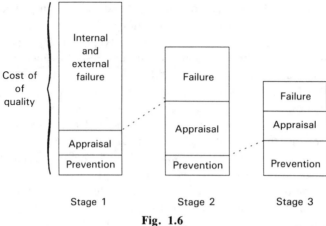

Fig. 1.6

attention – and perhaps some consultancy work. The essence of his method lay in mobilizing and training the entire work-force in quality from top to bottom: quality is a management responsibility, but it concerns everyone. Once the necessary impetus has been given, and all eyes are riveted on meeting the requirements with zero defect, everyone should find the appropriate tools and resources to attain this common goal.

So far, every effort and mobilization had focused internally, beginning with production and the measurement of defects and errors. Towards the outside world and customers, attitudes had remained defensive and protectionist. The objective, it was thought, was to minimize problems, reduce minuses and take out an 'assurance' policy; to do what had been promised while reducing non-quality costs. Thanks to the quality assurance department, the customer would be guaranteed the fulfilment of that promise, or at least a reduction in the number of things he or she disliked.

Is it not possible, however, to aim higher . . . at customer satisfaction? Quality is, after all, a vital selling point. Quality is what the customer is looking for, what makes the difference, what he or she is willing to pay for. A new strategy of differentiation through better quality implies mobility and change. Past achievements are there to be surpassed.

1.3.3 The Quality Dynamics or the End of Vertical Models

The third stage of quality development follows the same lines as the previous one. Again it includes responsibility and constant progress towards zero defect or zero error. However, the attitude towards the outside world becomes more offensive than defensive. Quality must no longer be perceived negatively by the customer (as being costly, unhoped-for or lacking) but, on the contrary, should be considered as legitimate, expected and desired. Quality must be perceived and considered positively. What the customer is actually looking for in the product or service should no longer be affected by considerations of faults or defects. Quality thus becomes a way of differentiating the product or the service. In fact, even more than mere customer satisfaction (a somewhat neutral, technical term) quality, to use Tom Peter's expression, should thrill and delight the customer.

The customer, then, should occupy a central place. The voice of the customer should be transmitted horizontally throughout the corporation. Quality is the link between marketing, engineering and production, an integral part of the business strategy. Quality will help to win market share and customer loyalty, and create barriers to entry. Furthermore, as customer needs grow and fluctuate under the influence of competition, quality targets must be stepped up and the rest of the organization rapidly realigned to achieve these new goals. Quality must keep its momentum. A quality dynamic must be set in motion.

1.4 MORE OF THE HISTORY OF QUALITY, OR JAPAN LOOMS AGAIN

The history of the quality movement in Japan, as recounted by Kaoru Ishikawa or Masaaki Imai, began at the end of the 1940s when the country was struggling to reorientate its war industry towards the export of manufactured goods. An export strategy was essential for a country without natural resources, and which imported a major share of its food requirements.

At this time, Japanese industry used the same technological processes as in the West, though the quality of the goods manufactured was mediocre and inferior to Western products. Japan did, however, have the benefit of abundant, educated and inexpensive labour.

The Japanese Union of Scientists and Engineers (JUSE) was founded in 1947 with the aim of supporting the reorientation of the country. In 1950, in response to an invitation by the JUSE, Doctor Deming, an expert on quality, gave a series of seminars focused on what was to become statistical process control (SPC). According to what became known as Deming's wheel (PDCA, or Plan, Do, Check, Act), everyone was responsible for improving their own production process. Dr Deming stressed that from the start, quality had to be a top priority. In 1951, the Deming Prize was established to reward firms with the best quality organization and results. Deming became a living legend in Japan, where 1950 is considered the year that the quality movement was launched.

It should be noted that during these seminars in Japan, Deming who was known only by quality control specialists in his own country, addressed chief executive officers and influential members of the Ministry of Industry. As Deming himself explained,

> The problem was how to reach top management in Japan. This hurdle was overcome through the offices of Mr Ichiro Ishikawa, President of the great Kei-dan-ren

(Federated Economic Societies) and President of JUSE, who in July 1950 brought together the top twenty-one men in management. Further conferences with top management were held during the summer of 1950, and on two trips in Japan in 1951, another in 1952 and others in subsequent years. The consumer is the most important part of the production line. It would be necessary for Japanese management to stand behind the performance of the product, to look ahead ... It will not suffice to achieve brilliant successes here and there. Disjointed efforts will have no national impact. Quality immediately became company-wide and nation-wide in every activity. (1986, pp. 488, 489)

Statistical process control was rapidly adopted in preference to statistical acceptance sampling (military standards). From the beginning, the approach was customer-orientated and customers do not like taking risks, even in the name of statistics. When a customer buys 100 parts, he wants 100 good parts. Zero defect quickly became the objective, even if the journey was long and initially costly since the company had to invest in final inspection before it was able to understand, control and improve its processes. In 1954, Juran visited Japan, also at the invitation of the JUSE. He positioned quality as an essential management mission. Quality, he taught, should be built in as a spiral, involving all departments, from design to after-sales. The objective is then to involve and train every manager in every department in quality improvement, concepts and methods.

Because in Japan top management and managers were made responsible for quality from the outset, the quality department never took on the importance that it was to assume in the West. Quality assurance did exist, but was a discrete department with a relatively small staff. After all, quality was seen as the responsibility of everyone.

Until the early 1960s, Japanese exporting firms trained all their managers in quality and, since the idea was contagious, they also trained their suppliers. In November 1960 the National Quality Month was inaugurated. In the following years, training swept from the top down to supervisors, front-line employees and workers. In April 1962 the JUSE launched the review *Quality control for the foreman*, edited by Dr Kaoru Ishikawa. The first quality circles became operational in the same year. They grew out of the need for the quality training of operators to be based more on practice than on concepts. Group work was therefore encouraged to solve local workshop problems, and quality circles were born. In this way, the corporation was able to integrate every initiative all the way down to the workshop.

Quality soon became an important dimension of management both inside the firm (the involvement of all, ownership and improvement) and outside, where it proved to be a formidable competitive weapon. Better still, quality enabled a company to gain a lead of at least several years, for quality is not so much a technological advance as a deep cultural change, which takes a long time to permeate right through an organization.

Under the leadership of its director, Kaoru Ishikawa, the JUSE played a major role in diffusing the new methods. In the 1960s and 1970s, widespread training was given in statistics, problem solving and process control methods. In the 1970s and 1980s, as a logical progression, quality left production to enter the areas of engineering and design. Quality had to be built in right from the start, when a new product or new process was being designed. This meant more time needed to be spent on prototypes, looking into potential problems, testing, testing and retesting, facilitating and simplifying manufacturing and delivery operations.

By developing simple plans of experiments, Taguchi popularized the analysis of variance methods in design and engineering departments. The match between the customer's needs and specifications was improved by value analysis, or tools such as 'quality function deployment' or Taguchi's tolerance and performance optimization methods.

As this brief historical overview has demonstrated, by readily adopting management responsibility, and understanding the strategic importance of quality, Japanese exporting firms induced a much faster quality dynamic than their Western counterparts.

Juran often uses the graph in Figure 1.7 to show the comparative development of quality in the West and in Japan. It took Japan twenty-five years of sustained effort to catch up with the West. Similarly it will take many years before those Western corporations now setting up total quality see their endeavours bear fruit. The competitive edge obtained by quality, it should be realized, is consolidated and amplified by its own dynamic. Many firms in direct competition with Japanese companies have been forced to make vigorous efforts to catch up in order to survive. For those who have succeeded, this is the proof that total quality is a universal method – and a model which travels well. As Figure 1.7 illustrates, 1975

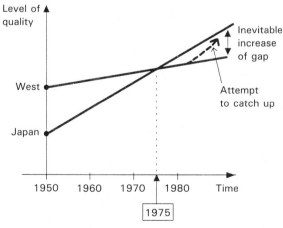

Note: Adapted from J. M. Juran, 'Product quality – a prescription for the West', *Management Review*, June–July, 1981

Fig. 1.7

was the real turning point for Japan. In that year, the efficiency of the Japanese export strategy clearly emerged, and began to impinge on the consciousness of Western companies. The following examples demonstrate this effect.

1.4.1 The Television Battle

Colour television was one of the first big battles waged by the Japanese export industry. The sequence of events in the United Kingdom provides a good example of what was a common scenario in many countries at that time. The graph in Figure 1.8 represents the percentage of exports of television sets by the United Kingdom and Japan compared with total exports by the industrialized countries (OECD).

During the period of latency, 1965–75, two or three competitors were emerging in the relatively protected Japanese market – producers of reliable products, with a quality of conformity aimed at zero defects and stabilized production flows based on just-in-time. Low costs (which dropped even further with the advantage of relatively cheap labour) and quality gave Japan a formidable competitive advantage. The Japanese then opened their frontiers, and their television sets flooded foreign markets. This is the so-called cocoon strategy, whereby the cocoon protecting local industry opens up once local industry is ready to fight on the international battlefield.

Television was invented in the West, but it was in Japan that the efficient production and quality control methods developed. In accordance with Juran's prediction, these were to bear fruit from 1975 onwards. It is, incidentally, reassuring to note that Western corporations like Thomson or Philips have since

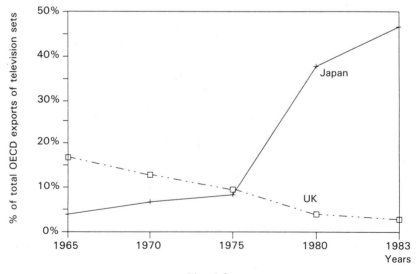

Fig. 1.8

shown themselves capable of taking up the challenge, though the battle is still raging.

1.4.2   The Battle of the Motorcycle

The motorcycle story provides an even more striking example. Again, among several that could be cited, the UK industry provides an illustration. (See Figure 1.9.) Some readers will still remember those splendid British motorbikes, so frequently in the repair shop: Triumph, Norton, DBK or the legendary French single cylinder 'Vélosolex', whose production ended in the early 1970s just when Hondas were beginning to invade the United States and Europe.

By 1983, Japanese manufacturers held 93 per cent of the UK motorcycle market. This is what fans would call a terrific kickback! Even those who once viewed the motorbike as something to tinker with continually and to soup-up, today swear by tamper-proof engines, thanks to electronics and modern sophistication.

1.4.3   Automobiles

In the automobile industry, regular surveys allow the number of incidents during the first year of guarantee or the first 20 000 kilometers to be monitored. A 'TGW' (things gone wrong) indicator measures the number of incidents per hundred vehicles. In recent years, this indicator has varied between 200 and 500 per hundred for Western cars (i.e. two to five incidents per car on average) depending on the model and time after launching. For Japanese cars, by contrast, the indicator has ranged from 200 to less than 100. This quality level, combined with productivity

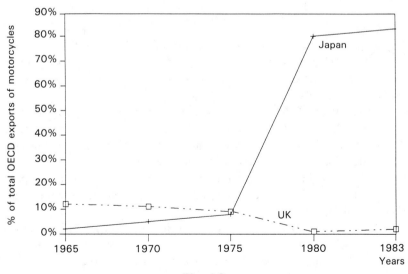

Fig. 1.9

levels two to three times greater and shorter development cycles for new models, provides a clear understanding of how and why Japanese auto makers have penetrated the entire Western market.

1.4.4 The History of Quasar

In 1974 Matsushita Electric Industrial Company purchased the Franklin Park, Illinois plant, which made radio and television sets under the Motorola brand (Ossela, 1981). It created the Quasar Electronics Company and restarted the plant with the same staff, but using Japanese management methods. Between 1974 and 1980, the following changes occurred:

● The internal failure rate (before final inspection) plummeted from 140 per cent to 5 per cent (a set could have several defects simultaneously) with a productivity gain of 30 per cent.

● The external failure rate, corresponding to claims during the warranty period, fell by 90 per cent.

● Early mortality (during the first hours of operation) dropped from 2.6 per cent to 0.32 per cent.

● The number of repair workers and defect analysis technicians was down by 75 per cent.

Of course, this turnaround was not due solely to Japanese management methods. The design and a certain number of components were directly imported from Japan. It is important to note, however, that it took place in the United States with a US work-force. Since then similar examples have multiplied.

1.4.5 Garvin Study

In order to compare levels and costs of quality in the United States with those in Japan, Garvin (1983) took the example of an air-conditioner, a relatively standard consumer product manufactured in both countries using relatively similar equipment and assembly lines.

The essential results of the survey, which covered seven Japanese and eleven US firms during the first two years of the 1980s, are summarized in Table 1.3. Furthermore, firms which had improved their quality increased their market share five times faster than firms where quality had declined.

Quality, cost reduction, differential advantages, market share, profits and investments: the logic is simple, disciplined, not particularly revolutionary but potentially lethal.

In the following chapters this logic and its dynamic will be analyzed to demonstrate that it is within the reach of any firm which makes a serious effort to do so. First and foremost, however, Western firms must get rid of their complexes *vis-à-vis* the Japanese model. After all, many firms that wasted no time in taking

Table 1.3

	US	JAPAN
Average internal defective rate (production line)	63.5%	0.95%
External defective rate (warranty period)	10.5%	0.60%
Average warranty costs	1.8–5.2% of sales	0.6% of sales

Table 1.4

Competitive priorities by order of importance		
Europe	United States	Japan
Consistent quality	Consistent quality	Low price
High performance products	High performance products	Rapid design changes
Reliable delivery	Reliable delivery	Consistent quality
Rapid delivery	Low price	Reliable delivery
Low price	Rapid delivery	Rapid volume changes
Rapid design changes	Rapid design changes	High performance products
After-sales service	After-sales service	Rapid delivery
Rapid volume changes	Rapid volume changes	After-sales service

up the challenge have succeeded brilliantly. They are living proof that success and quality do exist in the West. And as far as they are concerned, Japan has nothing more to teach them. However, the last round has yet to be fought.

1.4.6 Flexibility, or the Next Battle

A survey comparing the competitive priorities of production managers in Europe, the United States and Japan, showed that the quest for high quality and cost reduction is not the last stage of the journey (de Meyer *et al.*, 1989). The new battle looming on the horizon is flexibility. The Japanese are now making combined flexibility and low prices an investment priority, as Table 1.4 reveals.

CHAPTER 2

•

THE DEFINITION OF QUALITY

2.1 WHAT DO WE MEAN BY QUALITY?

Whenever groups of consumers or business leaders are asked to define quality, they invariably come up with a wide range of suggestions. A typical sample of these is given below.

Quality means:

- no problems, you can forget about it
- works so perfectly you never think about it
- made with great care and attention
- contract specifications, budget and deadlines are respected
- functional, user-friendly
- a fast, suitably adapted response
- a reliable product, long-lasting, cheap to use, robust, easy upkeep
- unique, excellent, beautiful, perfect, superb
- style, appearance, sophistication, top of the range.

As these responses demonstrate, while quality may prove itself in use, it also provides psychological or even aesthetic satisfaction, the feeling that the product is up to expectations and the customer has not been cheated. Quite clearly, the quality concept spans an extremely wide range.

Quality is first and foremost conformity to specifications. It is also a response adapted to suit the use required not only at the time of purchase, but in the long term as well. But in addition, it is that plus in attractiveness and excellence that makes it closer to desire than to actual needs.

Before attempting to map out the various meanings of quality we must quickly mention the other dimension that is almost inseparable from quality; the price of the product or service. This will be treated separately.

In Figure 2.1 two perpendicular dimensions clearly display the compromise between a price increase 'ΔP' and an additional advantage 'ΔQ' in the form of a quality differentiation, the effect of which can more than offset the price increase. Clearly, the supplier must always balance his books; the quality advantage given

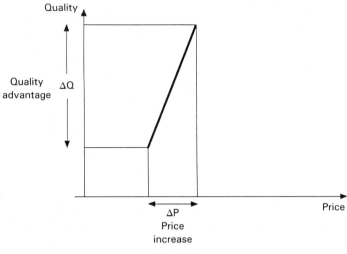

Fig. 2.1

should not be unduly costly, and in some cases it may even be possible to obtain better quality at lower cost.

The custom of trading a quality advantage for a price increase has resulted in the firm conviction that quality is expensive. This is expressed in the well-known Quality/Price ratio or by the concept of value, the internal scale measuring what is received and perceived versus the price we are willing to pay. Using this mind-set, quality appears to work on the second dimension, enabling a product or a service to be differentiated. This is an infinitely more mobile and complex dimension than price.

Which definition of quality should we adopt? Conformity? Performance and utilization? Attractiveness? Far from being contradictory or mutually exclusive these various definitions are, in fact, complementary and fit in with each other perfectly. Conformity to specifications is, of course, the basic one, but those specifications should also be related to customer requirements and a given utilization. Once the fitness for use is achieved, the offer has to be made better and more attractively than the competition. Put all these together and you have it in a nutshell: the offer, the customer and the competition. The sequence sounds right, but to make it more explicit, it is worth applying it to the development of a new product or service.

2.2 CUSTOMERS' NEEDS AND THE OFFER: SQUARING THE CIRCLE

Let us begin with a selected segment or target, a more or less homogeneous cluster of customers, to be satisfied by the offer of a product or service. We shall represent the target by a circle and the offer by a square. The task of the marketing and

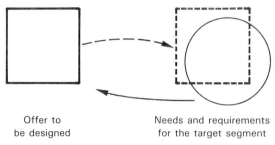

Offer to
be designed

Needs and requirements
for the target segment

Fig. 2.2

design teams is to position the square on the circle so as to cover it as fully as possible. This match or fit is represented in Figure 2.2.

Within the target segment selected for its size and potential, growth rate and 'penetrability', customers are assumed to have similar needs and expectations with regard to quality and price levels. The challenge for our firm is to cover expected performance levels better than the competition, by using its resources to the optimum. Let us consider the target segment in terms of its profile of needs.

2.2.1 Profile of Needs

Two difficulties should be stressed: the customers we are interested in are end-users, (in some cases the buyer is *not* the end-user). Furthermore, customers or users do not always know what they want or what they need. Before the arrival of the microcomputer, for example, very few customers would have been capable of expressing their need for a microcomputer. The needs and segments covered only appear clearly once the product or service is on the market – this is known as the 'ikiwisi' syndrome (I'll know it when I see it).

But what are the needs of the customer? We can take a classification of seven main dimensions.

Functional Performance and Usage

These are the basic performances and functions of the product: a shampoo that cleans and softens the hair; a car that provides the expected degree of acceleration or comfort; shirts that are the right shape and size; rolls of newsprint that do not tear in the machine. These functions encompass both the final characteristics of the product and the customer's expected end-use.

Safety

Naturally, the customer expects to be protected against the dangers that might be associated with the product's use, or malfunctions in service. In some sensitive areas, an abundance of regulations and standards covers these concerns.

Conformity to Promises and Expectations

Compared with its promised performance level, the actual usage of the product should not disappoint the customer with a 'minus' point – an error, a problem, a failure or a malfunction. A shirt should not feel scratchy; a shampoo should not make the eyes sting or trigger off an allergy. Contract specifications should be adhered to; the television picture is expected to remain sharp and flicker-free; the hotel room should be clean and the bed comfortable; the plane should leave on time, etc.

Availability

Reliability. The probability of the equipment or system breaking down within a reasonable time interval should be as low as possible.

Maintainability and after-sales service. In case of failure, the equipment or system should be easy to repair or to service. Repair or servicing time should be as short as possible. The same applies to cost.

Durability. The service life of a piece of equipment is an important factor, quite independent of frequency of use. For example, an equipment item may be corrosion-proof.

A 'Plus' of Service and Usage (Serviceability)

- The product is easy to install, easy to use (user-friendly).
- The product is available from stock or within a short delivery time.
- Assistance is built into the design, ordering, delivery, installation or usage stages.
- The product is easily adaptable (or expandable).
- Compatibility or interconnection with other systems is in existence or already installed.

A 'Plus' of Prestige or Attractiveness

Customers are affected by the design, the style and the image delivered. They like shiny, soft hair after a shampoo, a sharp television picture, detail and workmanship on their cars. They also appreciate receiving rather special treatment.

Nuisances and loss for society

While beneficial to the customer, a cost reduction may lead to greater countervailing losses for society as a whole, what are termed 'diseconomies', like pollution and nuisances.

Using these seven dimensions, a profile of the target segment's requirements can be drawn. Marketing and design will then define a suitable offer.

2.2.2 Positioning and Defining the Offer

Clearly, it is never possible to satisfy all the needs of a target segment; a certain discrepancy between the offer and the target will always remain. However, by selecting specific dimensions or functions with a certain degree of coverage, a product manager can try to position the offer to achieve the greatest possible edge over the competition. He or she will not be aiming to be the best in every dimension, but rather choosing a battlefield that will match his or her own particular strengths and weaknesses.

Transforming the circle into a square corresponds to the translation of external requirements, constraints and the demands of commercial specifications, into increasingly technical and quantified specifications. This might be represented as in Figure 2.3.

A simple example to illustrate this problem of translation from external requirements to internal specifications is provided by Kaoru Ishikawa, the Japanese quality guru. The example features a newspaper printer, whose performance requirement for the paper he uses is that it should not tear in his rotary presses.

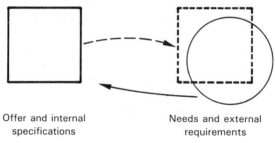

Offer and internal
specifications

Needs and external
requirements

Fig. 2.3

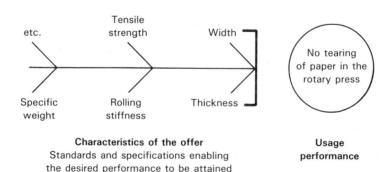

Characteristics of the offer
Standards and specifications enabling
the desired performance to be attained

**Usage
performance**

Fig. 2.4

Table 2.1

Needs, requirements			Technical characteristics and specifications				
Performance main functions	Sub functions	Importance	Thickness	Rolling Stiffness	Specific weight	Surface treatment	Etc
Easy passage through rotary press	No tearing	7	×	×		×	
	No folding	3		×			
Quality of print	Paper does not absorb ink	5				×	
	Etc.						

However, the best the supplier can come up with to satisfy him is to define the paper in three pages of technical specifications and features. These technical specifications, also called final characteristics, are supposed to satisfy the basic needs of the customer. They are represented in Figure 2.4 in a fishbone diagram, each branch corresponding to a given category of final characteristics.

Figure 2.4 can also be represented in matrix form, shown in Table 2.1, the performance dimensions, or needs as perceived by the customer intersecting with the final technical characteristics to be supplied. It is to be hoped that a strong correlation exists between the two (a cross or another sign can indicate the strength of the correlation). Naturally, the number and importance of the needs and functions covered by the offer will be based on the price the customer is prepared to pay, and on available or forecasted competitive offers. To achieve this positioning, very special attention must be paid to customer perception.

2.3 QUALITY OF DESIGN

Quality occurs when the offer matches the need, thus 'squaring the circle'. (See Figure 2.5.) Quality is not something absolute. Quality is what the client wants to pay for. 'To the client, quality is not free' (Ould, 1990). Only by actually seeing and

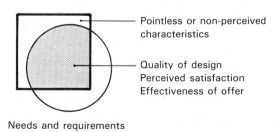

Pointless or non-perceived characteristics

Quality of design
Perceived satisfaction
Effectiveness of offer

Needs and requirements

Fig. 2.5

using the product, by 'hands on' experimentation, will the customer know whether he is as satisfied as he expected to be. Quality measures the degree of satisfaction perceived by the customer, the end-user.

Unperceived characteristics and performance are not part of customer satisfaction, which clearly demonstrates the importance of adequate customer preparation and information. Moreover, if certain characteristics are in fact pointless, their elimination can lead to cost reductions, unless we orientate the customer towards them. But to what extent is it possible to influence the customer so that he or she enters the square you are proposing?

If the product is error-free, we will call the perceived quality the quality of design, since it measures the match between the needs and the offer initially defined by the marketing and the design departments.

Quality of design is a measurement of offer effectiveness. It reaches its optimum by fitting the square onto the circle and then squaring the circle, something not that easily done, as mathematicians will testify. Quality of design can have several aspects, and good intentions are not always enough to avoid getting it wrong. A few examples will illustrate this.

2.3.1 Steinway and Yamaha (1981)

Both these are very successful piano makers, but in entirely different ways. Steinway decided to emphasize differentiation of quality by paying a great deal of attention to appearance, register, sound quality, touch and precise strike, and the maintenance of these features in the long term. These characteristics were achieved by reinforcing the design department, carefully selecting materials and components and using professional teams for production, while also remaining very active in the field and maintaining a high level of service.

Yamaha chose a different positioning. The performance level of Yahama pianos is less high, but they are in conformity with specifications; there are no defects, no surprises. The pianos are robust; the price is attractive. Considerable efforts have been devoted to production methods and reliability, so enabling after-sales service in particular to be reduced.

Figure 2.6, shows the two different profiles for two different segments of the market. In both cases the positioning is clear and fits the needs of their chosen customers. One firm has opted for robustness, conformity and reliability, while the other has chosen performance, sound quality and appearance over and above these basic features. However, a serious discrepancy could develop if the characteristics of either offer failed to take into account the requirements of the target segment.

2.3.2 Technical Narcissism and 'Over-quality'

Some equipment is capable of outstanding performance, or has highly sophisticated, automatic mechanisms likely to attract technicians eager to use the

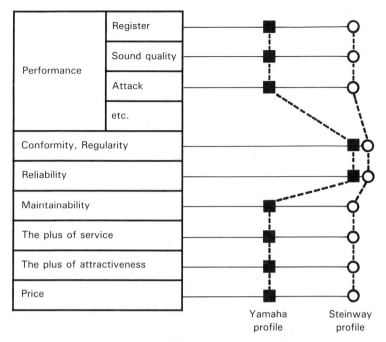

Fig. 2.6

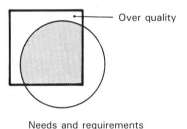

Fig. 2.7

latest gadgetry. However, these characteristics can prove to be pointless or remain unused, perhaps because the skills of their future users are inadequate, or because the equipment itself is being under-used to avoid breakdowns, or because the environment or technical support provided is insufficient. (See Figure 2.7). An example often quoted in this context is that of weapon systems, whose reliability decreases as their complexity increases; another is when over-sophisticated equipment is sold or donated to developing countries. This phenomenon is also visible in consumer goods:

● A new, deep-frozen dessert, produced in line with the tastes of the technician and product manager, fails to meet with the expected degree of success.

● A well-equipped clinic with ultra-modern, motorized beds is wasted if what the patients actually want is a warmer welcome from the staff, or a room where they can meet and socialize.

● A new mechanical razor with an ingenious blade-cleaning system may be revolutionary, but if the customer does not see the point of it, no advertising campaign on earth is going to convince him.

The pointless and gold-plating nature of these qualities leads to a design discrepancy: either the sphere of the need is ignored (first example), or its nature has been mistaken (what is the point of curing your patients if you leave them depressed, as in the second example). In other cases, the circle of needs has appeared to be impenetrable. Mistaken or egocentric designs are not the only mistakes that can be made. The absence of any real flexibility or adaptability can also lead to serious disappointment.

2.3.3 Standards and Adjustment to Needs

An emery paper manufacturer was losing market share. When he asked one of his main customers why he had gone over to the competition, he was given the following reply: 'Your paper just isn't competitive; the number of square meters used per 100 parts polished is much higher than for your competitors.' In this sentence, the customer articulated his selection criterion, which the manufacturer had never realized. All this time, he had merely been testing his product against the quality standards of the industry.

This example, cited by Juran, illustrates the pitfalls of living traditionally or routinely. By dozing on our habitual square we can lose touch with reality and the changing environment. Norms and standards are helpful, but inadequate if they fail to adapt or follow requirements. In some instances, standards may be no longer justified and to follow them will only lead to pointless extra cost. Nothing can be justified by the mere fact of its existence. As Kaoru Ishikawa said, 'Standards and norms are useful objectives and references, provided they are updated regularly every six months.' A product or a service only exists when used, which again emphasizes that quality is the result of uncompromising pragmatism.

2.3.4 Perception and Usage

After five years of design and development, a large corporation markets a domestic solar water-heater. Unfortunately, not only does the new product fail to meet with the anticipated enthusiasm due to its price and its inadequate performance compared with conventional water-heaters, worse still, several customers utilize this new water-heater to keep pre-heated water hot. This leads to considerable temperature variations and accelerated deterioration, which causes a large number of returns. After five years of development work, the company has suddenly discovered a new, unforeseen use for its product: 'We never dreamt anyone would utilize our product in that way!'

Similarly, a manufacturer of isolated copper wire failed with his product because he had not sufficiently tested his wire under service conditions with his customer (winding speeds, processing temperature or corrosive effect of the insulating oil).

Quality is revealed in actual use. This is even more the case once the product is better known and has become more standard. Usage can then be measured by the operating costs and service costs, or by life-cycle costs which sum up purchase and usage costs. For example, despite a high purchase price, a printer manufacturer succeeded in multiplying sales by demonstrating that the life-cycle cost or cost of possession for his printers was far less than for his competitors', due to greater reliability and lower power consumption. Quality of design means adapting the product to actual use. Helping the customer to adjust to using the product is another way of achieving quality.

2.3.5 Education and Customer Development

The first on a market, the pilot supplier, the developer as opposed to the follower, has the advantage of being able to define future norms and standards, which is one way of influencing and educating the customer. Satisfactory mutual adjustment can procure solid advantages. Sometimes, however, this adjustment is inadequate and therefore unstable, thus opening up the way to a more perceptive competitor. (See Figure 2.8.) In the case of parts and equipment suppliers to the automobile industry, for example, the pilot supplier induces the customer to use his standards, and so imposes them on the competition. However, this edge can become a handicap since, as time goes by, the customer will grow accustomed to a product. This often makes it difficult for the supplier to update the product, or convince the customer of the need for change.

- Coca-Cola, for example, met with considerable resistance when it introduced a new formula, and was obliged to continue the previous one while marketing the new Coca-Cola.
- The magnetic discs used for data-processing sometimes show darker patches

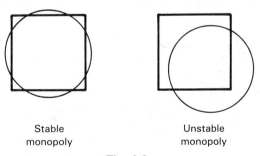

Stable	Unstable
monopoly	monopoly

Fig. 2.8

which in no way affect the recording quality. Would it not be preferable to inform customers of this fact, rather than scrapping these discs?

Advertising and contacts by the sales or after-sales force can contribute significantly to customer evolution and to a better perception by the customer of the advantages of a product. This often involves pseudo-scientific demonstrations to prove, for example, the superior cleaning power of a washing powder, the longer lifetime of a battery brand, or the closer shave obtained with a new razor.

The above has demonstrated several aspects of the dimension of perception, and the difficulties that may be encountered in defining and quantifying the offer. The next section will consider the efficiency aspect, i.e. fulfilling the promises made by the offer.

2.4 QUALITY OF CONFORMITY

Once the product has been defined and its final specifications and characteristics adopted, it must be designed in detail and manufactured. This is the field of engineering design, industrial engineering and production: a series of concrete transformations. Non-conformity measures the deterioration between the initial project and the product or service actually delivered. What is important at this stage is to realize the promised offer, the perfect square. (See Figure 2.9.)

If an error, a mistake or a failure, let us call it a 'minus', appears, an inspection system will have to be set up to filter it out and so avoid a perceived external failure. This inspection system leads to an appraisal cost. Correcting this minus value will lead to repair, rework or waste, not to mention scheduling changes, loss of time and additional inventory; i.e. an internal failure cost. Should this 'minus' reach the customer, it will lead to even greater repair costs by the after-sales service (and this may or may not be covered by the guarantee) hence there is an external failure cost, quite apart from the customer's negative experience which may induce him or her to switch to the competition definitively. But this 'minus' could have been avoided in the first place if precautionary measures had been taken. These would have appeared as a prevention cost.

Thus poor quality, represented by the minus area in the square, can lead to considerable costs, the sum of which is known as the cost of quality. As shown

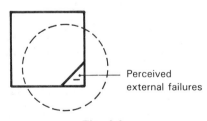

Fig. 2.9

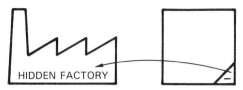

Fig. 2.10

in Figure 2.10 this is our 'hidden factory', producing defects and unsatisfied customers, and it is going to haunt the square.

To poor quality we must add non-values, i.e. all activities not contributing directly to the useful transformation: storage, packaging, handling, data-processing or excess management. It is as though, when delivering a car, the manufacturer filled it with all the packagings, computer listings, defective parts, waste, etc. involved in its manufacture and told the customer 'You bought all that with your car!' The client is certainly not ready to pay for these extra costs.

Such a display of non-added values may sound absurd and faintly amusing. But the final bill is perfectly credible and hefty:

    Costs of prevention
  + Costs of detection
  + Costs of internal and external defects
  + Redundant or needless functions
  + Needless processing and procedures
  + Wasted time.

In summary, quality of conformity measures the efficiency of the transformation process. Let us illustrate this concept with a few examples.

2.4.1   The Rolls-Royce and the Renault

Quality is often confused with excellence. But can we, for example, say that a Rolls-Royce is of better quality than a Renault? With a design and performance vision the answer is yes, and in this case better performance (power, comfort) must be paid for. (See Figure 2.11.) But with a conformity vision, the answer is no, if the specific Rolls-Royce has more defects than the Renault. The two views are reconciled when we consider the customer's needs and the price he or she is prepared to pay. Then it emerges that there are, in fact, two different targets, and each offer must be adapted to the requirements and conditions for use of the customers in each target segment. Hence, good quality products are not necessarily the most luxurious ones, when quality means conformity. Clearly, there are many more requirements for the Rolls-Royce than for the Renault (as shown in Figure 2.11): the Rolls-Royce is of better quality (of design) than the Renault.

But assuming that offers are well fitted to customer needs, there remains the

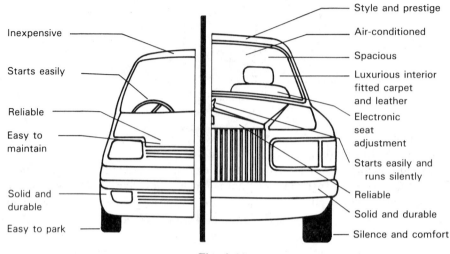

Inexpensive

Starts easily

Reliable

Easy to maintain

Solid and durable

Easy to park

Style and prestige

Air-conditioned

Spacious

Luxurious interior fitted carpet and leather

Electronic seat adjustment

Starts easily and runs silently

Reliable

Solid and durable

Silence and comfort

Fig. 2.11

problem of conformity. If one of the offers contains more defects, more 'minuses' than the other, it is of lower quality (of conformity).

2.4.2 The Modification Roundabout

In fact, non-quality can worm its way into every stage of product or service execution. Take, for example, a machine-tool manufacturer who has developed a new model which comes up with an unforeseen problem just before launching. As a result, the development department launches an emergency engineering modification.

Modification 1: changing a filter
Cost: modifying drawing, tooling, inspection, assembly/disassembly, testing
Time: three months, but selection of the filter material was erroneous. It is
    deteriorated by the cooling oils.

Modification 2: change of filter material
Cost: raw materials, tooling, inspections, assemblies/disassemblies, testing
Time: two months
Result: the filter functions satisfactorily, but the assembly of the subassembly of
    which it is a part has been automated in the meantime, and the filters entangle
    in the vibrating bowls. To avoid the need for an extra person to deal with this
    problem, the filter will have to be modified all over again.

Modification 3: alteration of the filter to be mounted on feeding cartridges
Cost: materials, tooling, testing
Time: two months.

Result: satisfactory, but certain filter suppliers have much less expensive standard filters which would also be satisfactory, provided certain machine tool dimensions were modified.

Modification 4: modification of certain machine dimensions and outside purchase of filters.

These successive modifications, which could have been avoided by an overall review and good planning, will all lead to extra costs and delays which in their turn will reduce the planned profit margin and displease the customer.

2.4.3 Comparing Quality of Conformity and Quality of Design

Loss of conformity can also ruin the positioning of an offer. For example, a major manufacturer of air-conditioning equipment notes that his products are well received by customers and highly commended in trade press reviews. However, rejects, rework and guarantee costs bring the firm to the verge of bankruptcy. The problem in this case is not due to design, but to non-conformity.

In Figure 2.12, which is to be preferred? Situation I or situation II? The competitive advantage of the offer in situation II is outweighed by the 'minuses' due to defects and problems during use. Clearly, we need the two aspects together: the right product and the product right. Thus the quality concept reconciles marketing and production.

In the trade war between Japan and the West, European manufacturers have tended to develop sophisticated hi-fi equipment without achieving the levels of conformity and reliability demonstrated by their Japanese counterparts. The Europeans have emphasized the quality of design whereas for the Japanese, quality

Situation I

Situation II

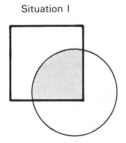 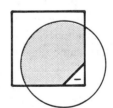

Poorly targeted offer with good quality of conformity. The offer is frustrating but works beautifully.

Situation preferred by manufacturing people: clearly the fault lies with marketing.

Better targeted offer with numerous problems of conformity. The offer is attractive but this makes disappointment in use even more frustrating.

Clearly the fault lies with production.

Fig. 2.12

of conformity has been paramount. However, even when full conformity in the offer has been achieved the battle is still not over. There remains a third factor to consider: the competition.

2.5 THE 'PLUS' OF DIFFERENTIATION

To maintain that quality means satisfying users' requirements with no defect or error is to adopt a neutral, not to say a passive and unimaginative attitude. Reducing claims and complaints is not enough to make customers vote in your favour. You must make their eyes light up with desire. For quality also means seduction, pleasure and delight, 'the passion for excellence' to repeat the title of Tom Peters' book. Quality is not merely the satisfaction of a contract duly fulfilled, it also includes the 'plus' which induces a customer to choose one product over another, one service rather than another. This is the plus which creates a difference between you and the competition, a differential wedge, a competitive edge.

Some dimensions of performance, usage and price are essential for customer satisfaction. However, if they are common to all products or services offered by the industry, they fail to create any real differentiation. They are important inasmuch as they may lead to non-satisfaction, and to minuses if they are poorly implemented, but the company must also look for marginal, but decisive, dimensions, capable of changing the consumer's mind. These are the pluses that will position their product or service to the company's advantage.

To win the battle, therefore, it is essential not only to ensure and consolidate a stabilized front, but to focus on a strategic advantage, a wedge that will enable you to penetrate the enemy front. (See Figure 2.13.) This advantage can be obtained by using minor, sometimes trivial dimensions, particularly if the product or service is already standardized and stabilized.

This is the case, for example, of the welcoming smile of airline stewards and stewardesses. Since an air ticket is just an air ticket, what difference can be created between the various airlines offering more or less the same services, on the same routes, with comparable levels of safety? The answer has been found in the secondary but determinant dimensions of the service given by the stewards and

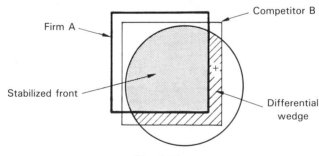

Fig. 2.13

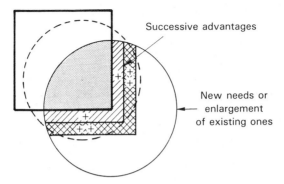

The dotted circle moves to its current enlarged position

Fig. 2.14

stewardesses, and hence the importance given to their selection and training. Just look at Singapore Airlines.

Unfortunately, if a competitive edge enables you to win territory and market share, the competition will not be slow in following, and you will then need to invent another difference: pre-check-in, more leg space, punctuality – all for the greater good of the customers with their ever increasing and changing needs. Thus the dynamics of competition help better to cover or modify the original target. This can be shown schematically as in Figure 2.14.

The quality dynamic is now under way. Firms must continuously create a new difference, and not rest on their past victories. This 'plus', this competitive edge must be based on the capabilities, skills and resources of the company. To achieve effective implementation, its existence must be communicated to all employees. To ensure clear perception, it must be communicated to the customers. The following examples illustrate how significant this differential 'plus' can be.

2.5.1 Something Can Always be Done, or Transforming 'Minuses' into 'Pluses'

- A single computer can always break down. Two computers, constantly exchanging their data, provide the reliability you need. This was the birth of Tandem.
- Chocolate-coated sweets dirty your hands, but Treets 'melt in the mouth and not in the hand'. Note the decisive importance of this relatively minor advantage, a simple coating in a bright colour. It focuses all attention on it, relegating the quality of the chocolate and other raw materials, the manufacturing process and packaging to a secondary role.

The Treets slogan, which had its hour of glory, is a good instance of the tricks which can be used to focus attention on a sensitive point. Turning a minus into a plus is sheer sleight of hand, zooming in on an advantageous detail to win custom.

2.5.2 A Decisive Detail

A large contract for unfalsifiable identity cards backed by sophisticated computerized systems was won because of the quality of the card layout, and reproduction of the photo.

2.5.3 Radical Superiority

In a plasma torch (very high gas temperature), the nozzle, the end-piece supporting the flame, wore out quickly. After two years' research, a Japanese manufacturer came up with nozzles lasting far longer and having greater accuracy. This superiority was so clear and so radical that many users went over to the new system because they preferred it even to other equipment with faster working speeds or thicker cutting capabilities.

2.5.4 Assistance to Users and Role of After-sales Service

Fortunate is the supplier who can provide customized assistance to his customer by analyzing the latter's expected use of the product or service. Such assistance can be integrated into various phases: design, preparation, transport, installation, information (ordering, shipping, types of use, manuals), repairs, maintenance, follow-up.

- By shipping chocolate in liquid form in specially designed tanks fitted to the trucks, a supplier helps his customer to reduce costs by eliminating the handling, unpackaging and remelting associated with bars packaged in aluminium foil for transport.
- By frequent deliveries to his customer within specific time limits, a supplier of integrated circuits enables his customer to operate just-in-time with reduced inventory.
- By installing a circulating document feed system combined with automatic stapling on a photocopier, Kodak simplifies the work of the user and reduces his costs.

There are a thousand and one ways in which the supplier can affect the life-cycle cost of a product during service. Frequently, however, managers refuse to recognize the importance of this service dimension. In such cases, outside market research can throw more light on the subject.

- Through a market research study performed by an outside body, a firm selling relatively sophisticated measuring equipment discovered that their customers considered the assistance and service provided for certain specific uses to be of major importance. To their consternation, they also discovered that for this dimension they were at the bottom of the list compared with the competition (to the particular surprise of the design and development department, which was unaware of, or did not take into account, its customers' needs).

As industrial products gradually stabilize and standardize, the service dimension assumes increasing importance. However, the provision of such services to the customer, and a stronger supplier–customer relationship, need not necessarily cost more.

● A cardboard manufacturer decided to install microcomputers on his customer's premises with a computer-aided design (CAD) software package. The customer then designed his own new packaging, selecting colours and printing patterns within the supplier's constraints which were built into the software. The customer could also obtain an estimate through a calculation program that was part of the CAD package. When the customer was satisfied with the final result, he could then send it to the supplier immediately. Undoubtedly, the customer responsible for his own packaging would be more likely to be satisfied. Moreover, in this case the development time could be reduced from three weeks to a few days.

2.5.5 Tolerances and Nominal Values

A product or service is defined by the nominal values of the main characteristics: the diameter of a part or the departure time of an aircraft. Mass production of the part or the repetitive nature of the service leads to a certain variability or dispersion of results around this nominal value. This dispersion is expressed by the so-called normal law, when the actual process is under control.

By defining tolerances, the design engineer normalizes variation. The customer, however, wants a service or product that is as close as possible to the nominal value. I prefer my plane to leave exactly on time rather than ten minutes late despite the fact that, even with ten minutes delay, the plane is still considered to be on time according to current international standards in airports.

As we shall see later, Taguchi considers that zero defect within tolerance limits is no longer sufficient, and that one should strive to be as close as possible to the nominal value. For example, the variability of the ball bearings manufactured by a certain company is far less than current standards, or the customers' specifications. In this case and as shown by Figure 2.15, the ball bearings manufacturer can choose between monitoring his production less rigorously, and allowing variability to occupy the entire tolerance space (the dotted line in Figure 2.15), or continuing to reduce dispersion by improving the process, not necessarily by investing in new machines. In addition, by reducing tolerance, he will also acquire an advantage: the bearings will make less noise. This is a plus which it is in his interest to keep and use to attract customers.

Taguchi contends that reduced variation and, ideally, zero dispersion is an absolute imperative, justified by the overall long-term interests of society, even if the advantage is not all that obvious in the short term. To him, monitoring and reduction of dispersion are long-term advantages to be relentlessly pursued.

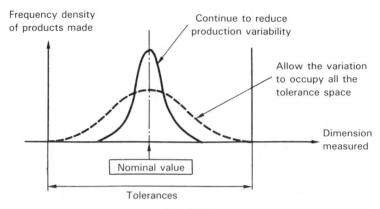

Fig. 2.15

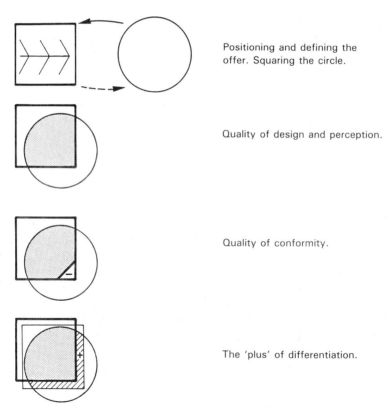

Fig. 2.16

2.6   THE FOUR STAGES OF THE QUALITY TRIP

Figure 2.16 summarizes all the foregoing by highlighting the four main stages of our voyage round quality. As will become clear, this four-stage tour involves all the previous definitions of quality.

The next stage is to tackle various definitions of quality, either official ones or those proposed by consultants, and test our model.

2.7   OFFICIAL DEFINITIONS

We shall begin with the standard definition of quality in ISO8420 (ISO means International Standards Organization):

> The totality of features and characteristics of a product, process or service that bear on its ability to satisfy stated or implied needs.

In this definition, quality measures the ability of the product, process or service to cover requirements as comprehensively as possible, simultaneously maximizing the perception of the offer and minimizing defects or errors. (See Figure 2.17.)

The Japanese Industrial Standards define quality control as follows:

> A system of production methods which *economically* produces quality goods or services meeting the requirements of consumers. (Ishikawa, 1985, p. 44)

As we have already stressed, the quality aspect can never be divorced from the economic aspect. While the above definitions cover all the various aspects previously mentioned, they are rather bland and lacking in that attractiveness and dynamic aspect which we have been trying to bring out.

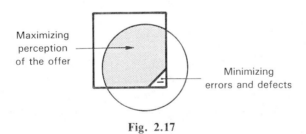

Fig. 2.17

2.8   CONSULTANTS' DEFINITIONS

2.8.1   Kaoru Ishikawa

Kaoru Ishikawa, one of the mentors of the Japanese quality school, offers the following definition:

> To practice quality control is to develop, design, produce and service a quality product

which is most economical, most useful, and always satisfactory to the consumer! (1985, p. 44)

Once again, we note that the economic aspect is inextricably linked with operations.

2.8.2 Philip Crosby

To Philip Crosby, quality is 'meeting the requirements'. The fact that he uses 'requirements', rather than 'needs' stresses the importance he attaches to the customer expressing his or her own needs. Needs must be specified; quality signifies the error-free achievement of these specifications.

Viewed narrowly, this definition only concerns the concept of conformity. Once specifications have been defined, quality means zero defect or error-free delivery. The danger of this approach is to concentrate too much on the square, on specifications, and forget about the customer. (This is why customers' needs are represented as a dotted circle in Figure 2.18.) If a Rolls-Royce complies with all the Rolls-Royce specifications it is a quality car. If a Renault 5 complies with all the promised specifications, it also is a quality car. Luxury, or the absence of it, is expressed in specifications: fitted carpets or rubber mats. Good or poor quality simply means conformity or non-conformity.

Crosby is so conformity-orientated that he could be accused of overdoing it, to the detriment of the dynamic aspect of customer perception. However, he does have the outstanding merit of being one of the pioneers, and of having convinced a large number of corporations that they must follow this cultural revolution. Conformity is the first stage of quality awareness and regaining the initiative.

2.8.3 Joseph Juran

To Joseph Juran, quality means fitness for use. The end-user does not always know the specifications. His assessment is based on the fact that the product is fit for use and will remain so. This is very similar indeed to the official definition, but this definition can be criticized as neutral or even passive. Quality can also be used for product differentiation.

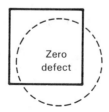

Fig. 2.18

2.8.4 Pat Townsend

Pat Townsend was responsible for setting up a total quality programme, named 'Quality has value', in the Paul Revere Insurance Company, in the United States (Townsend and Gebhardt, 1986). To him, quality is what customers perceive when they feel that the product or the service meets their needs and corresponds to their expectations. He distinguishes between quality in perception and quality in fact. Quality in perception is doing what needs to be done, the right product, the right service. It corresponds to effectiveness. Quality in fact is doing things as they should be done: doing the product right, doing the service right. This is efficiency.

To this two-fold aspect, quality of perception and quality of conformity, Pat Townsend adds the idea of expectation. The expectations of the customer are based on the promise communicated with the offer. (See Figure 2.19.) Thus there may be disappointment, i.e. an extra minus, if the perceived offer is inferior to expectations. This concept will be developed in Chapters 8 and 9 on quality in the services. The concept of expectation is particularly important for a service, due to its intangible nature.

2.8.5 Tom Peters

In his book *A Passion for Excellence*, Tom Peters vividly illustrates the dynamic aspect of extra quality attractiveness. His speech to the entire staff of Corning to celebrate the fourth anniversary of the launching of the total quality programme made it just as plain: 'We don't want to satisfy the customer, we want to thrill the customer, we want to delight the customer!' Satisfying is dull, uninteresting, flat. Passion is of the essence. Let desire transcend need.

2.8.6 Taguchi

Finally, to bring in ethics and the social responsibilities of the corporation, we turn to Taguchi for his definition. To Genichi Taguchi, quality consists of minimizing

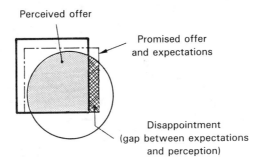

Fig. 2.19

the loss inflicted by the product not only on the customer, but also on society in the longer term. The main source of that loss is variability, the absolute evil.

Having gone from our 1 per cent level of defect culture to zero defect, we have now reached zero dispersion. We shall recap the definition of zero defect to explain this.

As Figure 2.20 suggests, design engineers usually define a tolerance interval around the nominal value of a characteristic (the value giving the best operational result). This is the zero defect interval, in which losses are supposed to be nil. Beyond this interval correction and repair are needed.

Taguchi disagrees wholeheartedly with this approach. For him, the slightest deviation from the nominal value means a loss proportionate to the square of the deviation. All products falling within tolerance limits are not equally good. The further away you get from the nominal value the more it costs, and even a slight deviation already represents a loss. (See Figure 2.21.)

Taguchi quotes the case of a manufacturer of vinyl plastic sheets used to protect crops. This manufacturer produced sheets at the lower thickness limit; the tolerance was 1 mm ± 0.2 mm, and his sheets were at the nominal thickness of 0.85 mm. He had achieved this through perfect control of the dispersion of his machines, instead of manufacturing at the nominal thickness of 1 mm as might have been expected. He has complied with the contract inasmuch as he has remained within the specified tolerance limits which range from 0.8 to 1.2 mm. (See Figure 2.22). The general verdict would probably be that the manufacturer was acting realistically; that he was 'a smart guy'. After all, his products are within the tolerance limit stated by the contract, and the market is tough.

Not as far as Taguchi is concerned. To him, this manufacturer is worse than a thief. Not only did his customers lose the protective sheets which failed to withstand the wind and tore apart, but their crops were damaged and prices rocketed. The manufacturer should have listened more carefully to the customer who wanted a nominal value of 1 mm. He should then have reduced the dispersion around this nominal value as far as possible, to the greater benefit of his customers.

If you want to be smart, you should ask your designers to carry out some experiments to discover the optimum operational values that will minimize loss (the flattest possible loss curves). Furthermore, should you succeed in reducing

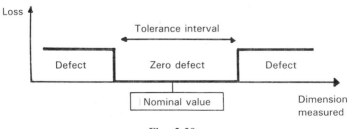

Fig. 2.20

dispersion, you are morally obliged to pass some of that gain on to the customer, because you sold him the nominal value and not the tolerance interval. Zero fault and zero dispersion at nominal value are economically sound and morally right. We have, it seems, uncovered a new dimension: quality is also moral.

In summary, if we had to add a definition to our four-stage model, we could say that:

Quality is the ability to satisfy needs at the time of purchase and during use at the best cost, while minimizing losses and surpassing the competition.

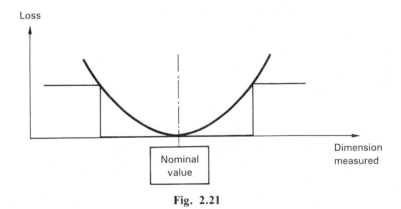

Fig. 2.21

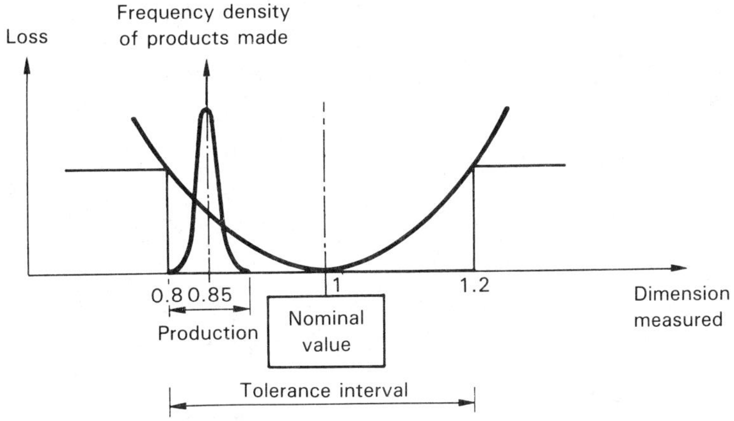

Fig. 2.22

PART II

•

QUALITY STRATEGIES

When describing the history and definition of the quality concept, we noted the emergence of the three main strategies:

- a corrective and defensive strategy
- an assurance strategy
- an offensive strategy.

We will develop these in the next five chapters.

A CORRECTIVE AND DEFENSIVE STRATEGY

Chapter 3: Quality as a Problem

In this strategy, quality control is used as the final barrier or filter before the product reaches the customer. As such, quality is perceived within the company as a necessary evil, a trade-off between different costs, a problem to be solved. In relation to the outside world, quality remains a defensive weapon.

THE FIRST REFORM: AN ASSURANCE STRATEGY

Chapters 4, 5 and 6: Quality as an Economic and Social Solution

While remaining externally defensive, quality here takes on a broader role. In this strategy, everyone within the company is mobilized to assure that the final product conforms with the promise made to the customer.

THE SECOND REFORM: AN OFFENSIVE STRATEGY

Chapter 7: Quality as a Strategic Solution

In this strategy quality becomes an offensive weapon. The efforts of every company employee are totally geared to fulfilling the customer's needs in order to build up a competitive advantage.

There is a clear link between all three strategies in that they correspond to a gradual awareness of the need to go beyond traditional management methods. By the final stage, management by objectives is no longer enough, and has been replaced by management for objectives. This implies a continuous search for improvement and the orientation of processes and systems towards customer needs before any attempt at cost cutting is made. In the following chapters, each of the three strategies will be analyzed at four levels:

the process
the corporate system
strategic vision
management of change.

CHAPTER 3

•

CORRECTIVE AND DEFENSIVE STRATEGY: QUALITY AS A PROBLEM

3.1 PROCESS CONTROL

A process is a series of operations leading to a given result: the final assembly of a unit or the sub-assembly of a component on a production line or in a workshop, the repair of an automobile at a garage, or the filling in of an invoice.

The traditional way of managing and controlling processes can be analyzed according to the five following aspects:

1. Division of labour and emphasis on productivity.
2. Quality control by final inspection.
3. Specialization of functions and low investment in process development.
4. Concentrating on controlling result. The status quo.
5. Improvement by radical restructuring.

3.1.1 Division of Labour and Productivity as Priority

Let us take a simple process such as the assembly of a climatic control system for a car on an assembly line. In accordance with motion and method study, the assembly process is broken down into standard elementary operations executed at a number of work stations. Each operator performs a specific job, planned and organized by industrial engineers and based on the specifications of design engineers. Execution and planning are clearly separated. The standardization of specifications and of work processes for each part is a necessary condition for the production of large volumes and productivity gains through economies of scale.

Taylor's approach to the division of labour and the standardization of jobs as a solution to mass production had, as its prime objective, the optimum use of people and machines. As a consequence, the worker or operator was seen as a cost to be controlled rather than an asset to be developed and a source of progress and initiative.

In this increased volume and cost reduction approach, the priority is clearly on productivity. The important thing is to work at full capacity, even though this implies multiplying the risk of breakdown, speeding up production processes to catch up on delays, and accepting re-work or scrap in all 'good conscience'. Quality plays a secondary role, and is in any case considered to be another department's job.

3.1.2 Quality Control by Final Inspection

Thus responsibility for quality belongs to others. At each work station the operator is simply asked to follow standards and procedures, with no incentive to co-operate with his neighbouring 'suppliers' or 'customers', and no direct responsibility for quality. As Hertzberg said, 'Can one reasonably make a human being responsible for an idiotic job?'

In this system, raw materials and parts from outside suppliers are checked by acceptance inspectors, flying inspection teams carry out random sampling on the assembly line, and end-of-line inspectors check the finished products. They all belong to the quality control department, which considers itself independent of production (after all, one cannot be both judge and jury) and serves as a protective barrier, though it is in fact a more or less selective filter.

The need for this filter has been imposed by the internal logic of a system which gives priority to volume and cost reduction through economies of scale. The aim is to ensure conformity to established specifications by following established procedures at a minimum cost, without any undue investment in process know-how or operator training. The rule is first and foremost to produce at the lowest possible cost; then inspect and sort if necessary. The overall structure for an administrative process is identical to the assembly line example given above. (See Figure 3.1.)

Setting up a filter does, however, represent extra cost: appraisal costs (i.e. labour, equipment, inventory, handling, transport, and data-processing), failure costs (i.e. scrap, rework) and therefore direct labour costs, loss of capacity and indirect costs (diagnosis, transport, storage), not to mention disruptions due to production delays and rescheduling.

Let us assume that after final assembly, the defect rate is 20 per cent. This level is not, it might be recalled, ridiculously high if the item is assembled in twenty or

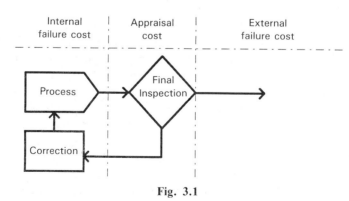

Fig. 3.1

so operations, with quality levels for each operation of the order of 99 per cent ($0.99^{22} = 0.80$). (See Figure 3.2.) However, this internal 20 per cent rate of defect is too high to be acceptable to the final customer and so must be reduced, at a reasonable cost, to the usual level of around 1 per cent. This means that the filter must be calculated so that the appraisal cost counterbalances the failure cost. Adopting this trade-off approach means abandoning all hope of reaching zero defect, for although at this level the failure cost will be nil the inspection cost will be enormous, as every single unit will have to be inspected.

The filter will not, therefore, be perfect. If it filters out 95 per cent of the defects, it brings the external failure rate after filtering down to the contractual level of 1 per cent, as explained in Figure 3.3. Note that 4 per cent of the units rejected by the filter are in fact good, but nevertheless have to undergo a second inspection, while 19 per cent are defective and have to be reworked.

To improve the final quality the filter must become more selective, which will in turn result in an increase in the cost of detection or inspection. This cost can reach significant levels if an attempt is made to go below a 1 per cent or 0.5 per cent defect limit, though in fact beyond this limit sampling methods require too large samples or become blind and lose all significance. The only alternative then is to resort to unit by unit inspection.

Demonstrably then, quality control acting as a protective barrier at input and as a filter at output is a necessary evil. In this case, quality remains the responsibility of the quality control department. What has been ignored is the fact that before becoming a quality problem, the defect was a design, industrial engineering, production or marketing problem.

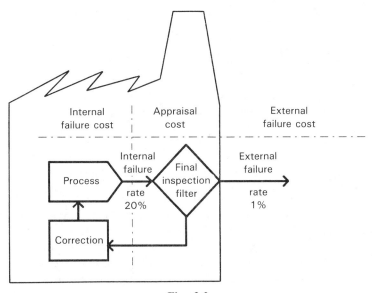

Fig. 3.2

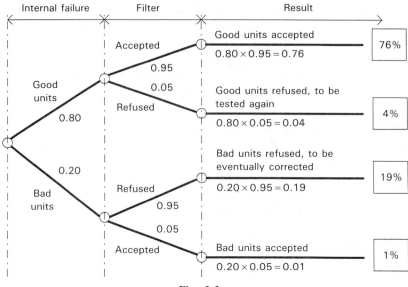

Fig. 3.3

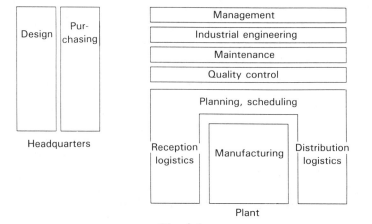

Fig. 3.4

3.1.3 Specialization of Functions and Low Investment in Process Development

As previously noted, the Taylorian approach to production implies handing responsibility for quality control over to specialists trained in statistical methods, measurement and testing. Similarly, engineering specialists carry out time and motion studies, define job procedures, and rate direct costs down to a ten-thousandth of an hour. Scheduling specialists plan work-loads, while breakdowns are dealt with by maintenance specialists who repair and service the machines, and logistics specialists optimize flows, inventories or transport.

As Figure 3.4 shows, such job specialization reduces the interaction between operators, and severely limits interdepartmental exchange. There is little or no direct horizontal or lateral communication between the various actors, and even less of a so-called supplier–customer relationship between one operation and the next. Once these relationships have been defined they remain virtually unchanged, and any unforeseen problems are sent up the chain of command. The experts who first developed these standards and methods of operation are not keen on updating or changing them too frequently, and more often than not are geographically isolated in offices or at corporate headquarters, some distance away from the operations. It should be noted that investment in process improvement is relatively low, once the investment in engineering and design has been made.

3.1.4 Concentrating on Controlling Results: The Status Quo

The product or service is thus delivered at an 'acceptable' conformity level after going through design and engineering. At this stage, however, despite the most stringent preparation, a certain level of poor quality will be present, due to lack of training, poor communications or unforeseen problems.

As a result, production starts up with a certain level of non-quality, and notwithstanding subsequent attempts to reduce it, an acceptable compromise will soon be found. The situation will then stabilize at this level for a variety of reasons. The production department, for example, has no reason to go beyond its prescribed task, and is anyway far too busy trying, in the face of breakdowns or modifications, to comply with schedules and costs. It has no time to worry about quality. As for the design engineer, he is already working on another more interesting project, and the same applies to all the other people who might be expected to be involved.

By default then, this quality level of the 'acceptable compromise' becomes the reference point for ordering components, raw materials or planning the utilization of resources. Any perception of non-quality gradually fades away, and the alarms are disconnected one by one. Recorded, accounted for, standardized, computerized, the process freezes at this level. Habits are formed, and this level of mediocrity is accepted by everyone concerned. All the operator has to do is to maintain the current level of performance, and stick to standards.

Should a sporadic problem occur at this stage, so causing the process to deviate from its habitual quality level, the supervisor or a 'fire-fighting' group will endeavour to bring the situation back to the status quo, the habitual level of performance. But what is considered normal or acceptable is a certain level of mediocrity, of poor quality, as part of the process remains hidden in a fog of ignorance. (See Figure 3.5.)

Adaptation to random variations and to 'normal' disturbances is accomplished by means of inventories or manoeuvring margins, built into the process by operators or clerks. These might mean a little filing to adjust the part, a little trick to make things work, or a 'personal' way of interpreting the rule. Adaptation in

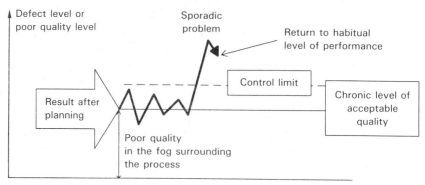

Fig. 3.5

this sense is more a sort of tinkering than a systematic drive for improvement. No one is prepared to invest in order to reduce uncertainty or to clear away the fog.

It has frequently been observed, for example, that no two shifts working on the same process will achieve the same results, and that neither adheres completely to the standards prescribed, supposing they exist. There may be two reasons for this: either the standards are poorly known and badly transmitted, or they have not been adapted or evolved with the changing situation. The necessary adjustments have not been made due to lack of time and resources. Functional staff have other fish to fry – productivity is their number one priority. In any case, it is out of the question for operators to be involved in defining or improving standards. They are there to do as they are told.

3.1.5 Improvement by Radical Restructuring

When the need for process improvement is felt, it is usually dealt with by large and not very regular reorganizations or rationalizations. (See Figure 3.6.)

Sporadic problems are generally solved by calling in line or staff managers to the rescue. However, there is little method in this type of problem solving, as the main objective is to get rid of the final symptoms without addressing the real causes. If it ain't broke, don't fix it. There is no accumulation of knowledge nor systematic recording of what has been learnt. The resolution of outstanding or repetitive problems must wait for the next reorganization or rationalization.

But when the next reorganization occurs (as shown in Figure 3.6), its main objective will be to reduce costs and increase volumes; and if at the same time quality levels improve – why then, so much the better. Productivity comes first, quality second. Moreover, between two reorganizations, the acceptable chronic level of poor quality obtained after the adaptation period will remain the reference, the objective to be attained. Clearly, this kind of management by objectives only serves to maintain the status quo.

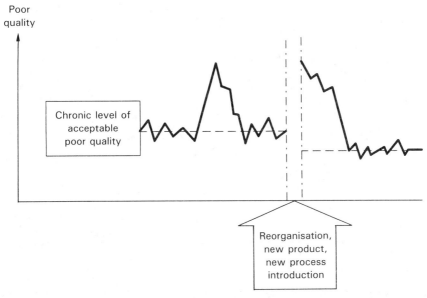

Fig. 3.6

3.2 SYSTEM CONTROL

As opposed to looking at individual processes, we will now consider the corporation as a whole. This section will examine the corporate system and the chain by which value is added: marketing, design, purchasing, engineering, production, sales and after-sales, not forgetting other functions such as finance or personnel. The same five stage approach can be used:

1. Cost control and priority to productivity.
2. Quality as a problem delegated to a specialized department.
3. Specialization of functions and non-co-operation between departments.
4. Control of results and status quo.
5. Improvement by radical restructuring.

3.2.1 Cost Control and Priority to Productivity

The standardization of specifications and processes enables the industrial fabric to be easily extended, and the company to operate on a large scale. To take advantage of economies of scale, companies grow rapidly in size. This quest for productivity is basic to any industrial organization, and is clearly demonstrated in the product–process matrix described by Robert Hayes and Steven Wheelwright (1979). A simplified version is reproduced in Figure 3.7 where I have added the notion of experience curve.

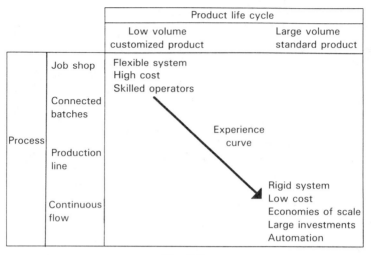

Fig. 3.7

In Figure 3.7 the horizontal axis represents the normal behaviour of a product or service, from its initial appearance in customized form with low volumes to its mature form, when it is standardized and produced in large volumes. The vertical axis represents the different processes of production, job shop organization, semi-connected batch production, line production and finally continuous flow (well-known examples are continuous casting, float glass, manufacture of chemical products or paper).

The natural path of evolution follows the diagonal line, starting with customized products in a job-shop type of organization, and inevitably ending up with highly standardized products and enormous volumes in rigidly controlled modes of production. This experience curve, which relates efficiency gains to increased capacity investment, has led to outstanding results and the so-called consumer society with which we are all familiar. However, the flexibility of the system and the quality of the result are inevitably and adversely affected by it. At a certain level of capacity, the lowest possible costs and adequate volumes are essential for survival. Quality, which is only considered after the battle is over, is merely the result of the best possible compromise between appraisal and failure costs. The product will be delivered on time, even at the risk of poor quality. Schedules will be respected at the cost of test experiments or the postponement of maintenance work, with the concomitant risk of greater variability in the product supplied or more breakdowns in production.

Management by objectives of cost and programme impregnates every single department. It is even transmitted to the suppliers because the purchasing department, obsessed by its budgets, tends to multiply the number of suppliers in order to enforce competition between them. The same approach permeates the design department. Savings are made in testing, developing, experimenting, even though this may result in numerous engineering changes at a later stage. During the industrial engineering phase, this approach leads to less time being spent on validating processes. First runs are launched, even if all the parts have not yet been certified. Machines are often purchased from all over the place (different models, different makes) because the priority in every negotiation is cost reduction. If the maintenance department is unable to follow and adapt to this variety, not to mention the spares inventory that must be carried, then it is just too bad. The personnel department, of course, recruits staff as cheaply as possible, for the labour force is considered a cost to be controlled rather than a source of human potential.

3.2.2 Quality as a Problem Delegated to a Specialized Department

As quality is not a priority, the realization of its importance only dawns at a later stage under pressure of a crisis, or following complaints from a dissatisfied customer. But who is then responsible? The usual reaction is to see quality as a problem to be dealt with by a quality control department containing experts in statistical sampling methods and reliability.

In a plant producing perfume bottles for example, the 'hot' production sector manufacturing bottles is juxtaposed with the 'cold' quality control sector. In the former department, ovens and complex machines are operated, supervised and maintained by skilled workers or technicians. In the latter, an army of unskilled operators is responsible for unit or statistical inspection, a task taken over by automatic sorting machines whenever possible. Production versus inspection, two worlds with very little interaction. Very few technicians will be interested in tracing problems back to the design, the mould, the machine or the production process.

3.2.3 Specialization of Functions and Non-co-operation Between Departments – A Parochial Attitude

The separation between staff and line personnel has already been noted. Functional staff organize, plan, design, manage and analyze information. Whether they work in design, marketing, engineering, maintenance, quality control or financial control, they all have their own field of expertise. See Figure 3.8. This knowledge endows them with a power that they will endeavour to keep.

In any plant, the operators depend for their productivity and their bonuses on machines that can and do break down. Therefore, the maintenance department, which is responsible for repairing the machines, holds a certain power over them. To communicate maintenance know-how would be to hand over that power. Besides, if the machines no longer failed or could be repaired by the operators themselves or the line personnel, they might be out of a job.

Based on this line of reasoning, each department, each sub-system, tends to isolate itself. It is the ivory tower or the 'silo' syndrome. Each department develops according to a 'squared' vision of its own particular universe, according to

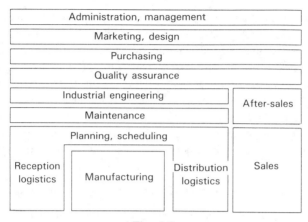

Fig. 3.8

'squared' specifications, even though this means losing sight of the needs of the next circle, the next internal 'customer' department and, last but certainly not least, the end-user. In this world, each department tends to measure and optimize its own results, and to regard its own problems as priority.

This lack of interdepartmental communication is particularly evident in the case of complex projects such as the launching of a new product. As the various stages follow each other in series with very little overlap, the result is a gradual loss of coherence that leaves a pile of unresolved problems at the end. The classical lack of communication between design and production is illustrated by the design engineer of a new product who throws the drawings file 'over the wall' separating his department from the production department. In fact, this wall often corresponds to a physical or geographical separation. And the production manager who receives the file screams: 'My God, they must be mad. Do they really expect me to make this thing?'

3.2.4 Control of Results and Status Quo

Another effect of this approach is that each sub-system, each department develops its own measurements and indicators of efficiency. Given the lack of lateral communication, little or no account is taken of changes in the requirements of the customers, either internal or external. As long as the environment remains stable or only changes slowly, this system functions satisfactorily. Any deviation in cost or volume objectives is quickly detected by the financial controller and the problem is solved by the hierarchy, whose main role is to reduce deviations and bring the system back to the standard, acceptable, chronic operating status.

In this environment, the need to change standards or procedures is perceived more as a problem or an unexpected crisis than as an opportunity. Any modification is still carried out through the chain of command, as it is necessary to climb fairly high to obtain an acceptable compromise between the departments involved. This trade-off will not necessarily favour the end customer. Segmentation perpetuates old and local objectives. Gradually, each sub-system organizes its own operating modes and develops its own protective environment with margins for manoeuvre, slacks or inventories in order to cope with uncertainties. Isolation is expensive, but the true cost of such poor adjustment between departments remains quite concealed.

Moreover, these managers are being judged according to their results: objectives achieved, budgets, programmes and quotas negotiated or fixed locally for their department at an acceptable quality level for the final product. These objectives are expressed mainly in terms of volumes and costs; the physical process is ignored. This is management by objectives or by results. Managers are satisfied with the status quo, with attaining objectives; they have no need to worry about investing further effort to improve the process.

3.2.5 Improvement by Radical Restructuring

Once standards, norms, objectives, quotas, yields and territories have been fixed it is difficult to change them, i.e. it is difficult to change the rules of the game. Above a certain hierarchical level, the management will not be aware of any possible improvements. Operators do not communicate any improvements they have made locally up the chain of command. They see no point in changing standards, and in any case are not expected to do so. With a bit of luck these improvements will give them more slack locally and a bigger margin for manoeuvre.

Improvement, when needed, will be the result of serious reorganization. This will be undertaken by technical staff investigating the operations, by financial auditors or by *ad hoc* teams of engineers and consultants, who will restructure and renovate the system or introduce new products and new processes. Progress is thus achieved by a succession of large steps and breakthroughs. (See Figure 3.9.) But this still leaves the corporate system imprisoned in a hierarchical, mosaic structure that will prove cumbersome to manoeuvre should the environment require rapid adjustments and greater interdepartmental communication.

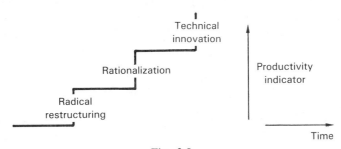

Fig. 3.9

How can the system be made more flexible, more reactive, more capable of providing the quality the customer expects to get first time?

3.3 MANAGING BY PROGRAMMES AND COSTS

3.3.1 External Vision: A Passive Approach to Quality in Step with the Competition

Traditional production systems are piloted by programmes and direct costs: delivering the product or service within the deadlines even if the result is not up to scratch, or reducing costs even if it means that the quality will be only just acceptable, and the customer likely to be disappointed.

In the above situation, which often corresponds to buoyant demand and established markets, quality is not perceived as a strategic dimension able to provide competitive advantage. Quality is merely seen as a problem to be dealt with by the quality control department. All is well as long as management does not hear about quality problems, as long as there is no crisis, no surprise and the quality level offered is in step with that of the competition.

The position adopted *vis-à-vis* the competition is defensive. Provided that this same status quo holds good for the entire industry, a culture of 1 per cent acceptable level of defect appears to be the best compromise between appraisal and failure costs. Of course, for critical or major defects the rules will have to be far more rigorous. But even then the aim is to avoid catastrophic consequences rather than to seek a positive competitive advantage or closer links with the customer.

3.3.2 Internal Vision: Quality, a Problem and a Necessary Evil

Senior Managers are Unaware

As far as top management and senior executives are concerned, quality represents compliance with certification schemes, parasitic taxes and inevitable costs. In the board room, quality management is perceived as a collection of production related techniques to be delegated to the quality manager. This low level of commitment becomes clearly visible if we compare the time senior executives spend monitoring cost and productivity objectives with the time they devote to quality problems, or if we observe the same production systems working at twice their normal rate during the last three days of the month.

Cutting Costs but not Managing Costs

Cutting costs and rationing resources can lead to false economies, as strategic customer orientation is lost to productivity imperatives. Cutting costs means taking short cuts, for example reducing direct labour, but without assessing the diseconomies generated in indirect costs such as extra inventory, poor quality that must be remedied later, poor use of equipment, etc. It often means uniform cuts, whereas a far preferable course would be to manage costs, that is to invest here (industrial engineering for example) and reduce there (inspection). Cutting costs means setting up a reactive management, more interested in short-term results and quick-fix solutions than in process and system improvement. It sometimes means reducing the value of the offer, or not adjusting to customer needs. Efficiency prevails over effectiveness, but in reality the price is high.

The Quality Objective is Opposed to Other Priorities

When quality improvement is imposed by customer dissatisfaction or by competitive pressure, management generally endeavours to get the message across by designating a new objective to be achieved. However, this message is often in conflict with former priorities, which remain unchanged. A trade-off must therefore be found.

How meaningful is the message that quality is essential, when the waiting truck is loaded with a batch of non-conforming products on the grounds of a 'commercial decision', when operators are reprimanded for batches returned by customers, when insufficient time is given to consider possible improvements to the system? What is the point of posters, slogans, exhortations and quality crusades, if the priorities are not clearly established and explained?

The System is Overmanaged but Underled

What is the point of designating the objective to be attained and appealing to motivation if the management is unable or unwilling to modify the system itself?

Poorly trained or overspecialized operators and employees have neither the margin of manoeuvre nor the means to reduce poor quality generated by the corporate system. It is the system itself that must be reformed. It needs more than managing and maintaining; it needs to be led in new directions.

The low level of senior management involvement, the interdepartmental barriers, the cumbersome chain of command, all these mean that every attempt to improve quality can only be piecemeal (setting up quality circles here or statistical quality control methods there). Change cannot be successfully implemented without an overall quality vision and direction at the highest level.

3.3.3 A Result-based Measurement System

The performance measurement and information system adopted is also result-orientated, reflecting management by programmes and costs.

A Trade-off Between Two Costs of Non-quality

As has already been explained, quality of conformity is the result of a trade-off between failure costs (scrap, repair and rework, warranty) and appraisal costs (inspection and quality control). When the number of defects tends towards zero the failure cost decreases regularly, while the appraisal cost increases rapidly. The trade-off is obtained by minimizing the total cost, i.e. the price the client is prepared to pay to obtain an acceptable quality level. At that point, both costs are equivalent, as is shown clearly in Figure 3.10. Beyond that point, better conformance would cost the customer more.

Costs of Poor Quality Difficult to Assess

In actual fact the costs of poor quality, particularly the failure costs, are difficult to measure by traditional accounting systems and tend to be substantially underestimated. These traditional accounting systems are better suited to an analysis within homogeneous sections, without cross-sectional views. Non-qualities are hidden at the boundaries between sections or between departments, and are therefore largely ignored. Moreover, fear of the consequences may lead employees to falsify performance information in order to satisfy their bosses.

Control by Productivity and Costs

As productivity is generally calculated by dividing total output, whether good or defective, by the factors employed (human or technical), the essential priority

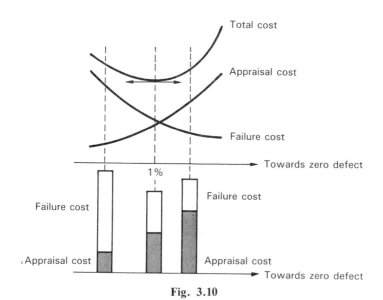

Fig. 3.10

remains volume. Similarly, cost control concentrates on short-term financial results and partially ignores the physical process or the delivery system. A dollar invested in process improvement, staff training or the certification of a supplier, is not equal to a dollar invested in inspection. While no one will deny the importance of controlling the final result, it is not everything. Investment in prevention and the improvement of the industrial environment is also essential.

Such a thought recalls the ironic comment of Masaaki Imai who, returning with a group of colleagues to the United States to take a second look at the steel mills and automobile plants they had photographed thirty years before, exclaimed: 'But nothing much has changed! They still look like the photos!'

3.4 STEERING CHANGE

3.4.1 Centralization and Stratification

The point has already been made that as the organization becomes more mature and the products more standardized, centralization and stratification, i.e. separation between functions, departments or territories, intensifies. Cross-departmental communication is less and less easy to achieve, and change is more difficult to manage. To solve dysfunctional or cross-functional problems it is sometimes necessary to go high up the chain of command, or to create specific co-ordination bodies.

3.4.2 Role of Management

Once each job, procedure, operation has been clearly defined and planned, the role of the manager is essentially to control and maintain the system, to hold it within limits, standards, rules, objectives, programmes.

As operators – and a fair number of executives – are not involved in the establishment or modification of these standards and operating procedures, and are often unaware of the ultimate aim of their work, they do not feel particularly concerned with quality of conformity or the satisfaction of the end-user.

Thus as the system becomes more bureaucratic and hierarchical, levels and classifications are multiplied and incremental change becomes not only more difficult, but also less welcome.

3.4.3 Communicating Change

In these situations change, as already noted, is formulated by specialists and then imposed from above through a major restructuring. These specialists do not specifically seek the co-operation of operators, though even if they were allowed to have a say, their participation would remain superficial.

3.4.4 Education and Training

For clearly delimited and finely divided jobs, relatively unskilled labour with a low level of education will be hired. Some operators will be trained on the job in a few days. Flexibility is ensured by hiring and firing labour, which is considered more as a work-force and a cost to be controlled than as human potential.

3.4.5 Recognition and Celebration

Those who get the awards and the medals are the champions, the Stakhanovites of productivity and sales. Medals will also be awarded to the trouble shooters, the fire fighters and crises solvers who are resourceful enough to prevent the assembly line from grinding to a halt.

CHAPTER 4

•

QUALITY AS AN ECONOMIC AND SOCIAL SOLUTION: PROCESS CONTROL AND IMPROVEMENT

We had sometimes burnt the toast and then scraped it clean, instead of fixing the toaster. Some of us had even learned to like burnt toast. (McDonald, president and CEO of Florida Power Light)

If quality is to be considered a solution rather than a problem, certain basic assumptions and traditional management methods must be completely reversed. This is a long-term process that begins with the concept of conformity to requirements and error-free work. With quality as the aim, the only acceptable level of achievement is excellence, with a probability of 100 per cent success.

To achieve this, the entire corporation must be mobilized. The method is simple and has been tried and tested: first, prevention and control to get things right first time, then improvement until excellence is reached. But as we all know, the road to excellence is a long one.

Quality will result from the gradual involvement of each and every member of the organization. As the dysfunctional aspects of the old culture become more visible, quality should become an increasingly important part of their daily work. However, this internal reorientation within a consistent framework, this internal mobilization, cannot be accomplished without the unconditional support and commitment of top management. For top managers, the pursuit of quality must represent a long-term investment, one that will lead to reduced costs while fostering the development of human resources. It should be pointed out, however, that at this stage the external strategy will still remain defensive, vigilant but passive. The aim is to assure quality and to reassure the customer.

In this chapter we shall analyze this change of orientation at the elementary level of manufacturing or service delivery processes. The following five aspects will be covered:

1.   Quality as a priority: process control through prevention and learning.
2.   Reintegrating quality responsibility into the process.
3.   Planning and prevention. Engineering quality into the process.
4.   Control and stabilization of the process.
5.   Improvement and maintaining the gains.

A process is a series of operations resulting in the delivery of a finished product or a service. Typical examples are a series of manufacturing operations to produce a part, or the processing of a client or a file. This process usually involves combining labour, equipment, information, raw materials and methods in order to attain a specific result.

4.1 QUALITY AS A PRIORITY: PROCESS CONTROL THROUGH PREVENTION AND LEARNING

The previous chapter showed how the standardization and economies-of-scale approach resulted in a loss of quality and flexibility. To break out of this vicious circle, the order of priorities must be reversed and quality placed at the head. This will not lead to any loss in productivity but rather to a broadening of the productivity vision. Investing in quality means investing in knowledge of the process upstream, in prevention, in know-how, in learning. Such an investment will be amply rewarded in the future through savings in inspection, failure, correction or guarantee costs, not to mention customer goodwill.

This need to reverse the order of priorities will be more readily understood in the light of the following demonstration of how we learn about a process, from its first definition through trial and error up until complete unsupervised automation. Three basic stages can be distinguished in the learning of a process, and these will be analyzed one by one.

1. Measurement of final characteristics and inspection.
2. Identification of key parameters and controlling the process.
3. Control of contingencies and preparing for automation.

4.1.1 Measurement of Final Characteristics and Inspection

At this first stage, the objective is merely to define the final characteristics and acceptance limits of the product or service delivered. The process itself may be poorly defined but, provided results are reasonably satisfactory, it will do for the time being. Where quantification is possible, each specification is expressed in terms of a nominal value and a tolerance range, showing the acceptable variation. On some occasions, however, quantification is so difficult that operators may be forced to make do with boundary samples and qualitative judgement. Whatever the case, the final result will remain binary: good or bad, result achieved or not achieved. To express a quality feature in a testable form, the definition must be precise enough to test that the feature has been achieved. According to Martyn A. Ould (1990, p. 100), when we specify for a software system that 'a warehouse employee shall be able to use the system confidently after two hours' tuition', the vague notion of confidence is not precise enough and should be replaced by, for example, 'without more than one error in twenty transactions over three hours' use with the agreed standard profile of work'.

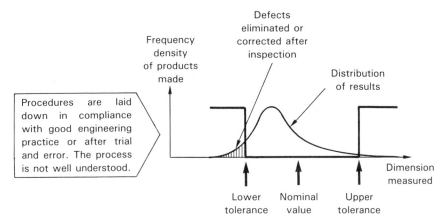

Fig. 4.1

The choice of equipment and operating procedures leading to the desired result is made by process development engineers. They make a technical choice based on efficiency criteria. As soon as results are acceptable, the process is fixed in that position to avoid any further investment of time and effort. Thereafter, all the operators have to do is follow the standard procedures and work sheets as defined. If the distribution of results goes beyond the predetermined limits, inspection and sorting will be carried out. After inspection and sorting, the resulting mediocre quality level will be justified by a certain level of ignorance about the functioning of the process, and an inability to do any better in the circumstances prevailing.

Inspection and testing are thus the price to be paid for ignorance about the process. However, though trial and error may seem a crude and inefficient method, it is the best if not the only solution possible when the process is not fully understood. (See Figure 4.1.)

4.1.2 Identification of Key Parameters and Controlling the Process

In order to change to a more scientific approach and hence improve the formula and the operational conditions, the main parameters affecting the result must be identified. At the beginning a large number of parameters might appear to affect the result, but on closer scrutiny only three or four determining variables may emerge. The well-known fishbone diagram, also known as the cause and effect or Ishikawa diagram, can help to isolate these few decisive parameters. (See Figure 4.2.)

Of course, many other methods such as systematic experimentation and correlation analyses can help to identify those process variables which condition the capability of the process. Once identified, the monitoring of these variables will directly guarantee the final result. Hence, control of results by inspection has been

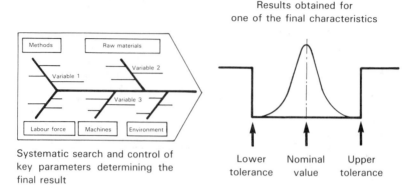

Fig. 4.2

traded for direct process control, and management by results has been replaced by management for results.

Maintaining these decisive parameters within precise variation limits, and complying with specific procedures and standards, will ensure that the final result is right first time, every time. The regular sampling of the final result, or measuring the first and last part of a run, will be enough to ensure that the entire production is right. Detection and failure costs are thus considerably reduced.

4.1.3 Control of Contingencies and Preparing Automation

Once the basic formula has been fixed, the next step is to reduce dispersion by further process improvements, and to achieve zero defect with a greater degree of certainty. As the sources of variation are more firmly controlled, so the process becomes more robust and better prepared for automation. The third step consists of controlling internal disturbances (wear, ageing) and external disturbances (temperature, environment, raw materials). Whereas previously we stuck to the basic formula and the nominal values, at this stage a more robust result is sought through optimizing the key parameters and their acceptable limits of variation. (See Figure 4.3 and 4.4.)

The process, now adequately controlled and impervious to disruptions, is ready to go over to unsupervised automation. The cost of poor quality will then be further reduced as controls are gradually integrated into the process itself. The lesson is plain; quality leads to automation and increased productivity, provided enough energy is invested in acquiring a better knowledge of the physical process. (See Figure 4.4.)

In summary, to achieve conformity and reduce variation it is essential to change from management by results to management for results by process control. However, this orientation implies an in-depth knowledge of the process. Inspection is traded for experimentation and learning. The knowledge thus acquired should

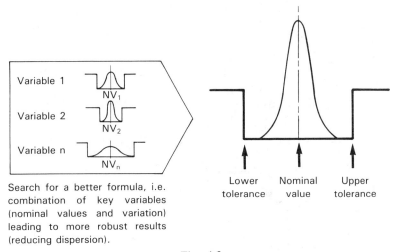

Search for a better formula, i.e. combination of key variables (nominal values and variation) leading to more robust results (reducing dispersion).

Fig. 4.3

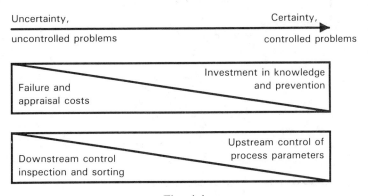

Fig. 4.4

not remain locked in people's minds but should be written down, formalized, standardized, used as a reference and transmitted. Therefore it is important to record it in the form of operational standards on control charts and operating procedures, an updatable file open to further improvement and enrichment.

4.2 REINTEGRATING QUALITY RESPONSIBILITY INTO THE PROCESS

The only way to obtain error-free results is to prevent problems and to control the physical process upstream. Control through inspection of the final results is far from being a satisfactory filter. Statistical sampling methods are not capable of screening defect levels below 0.5 per cent, while unit by unit sorting by inspectors is even less reliable. Extremely low error rates can only be obtained through automatic sorting methods. However, these methods are dependent on the

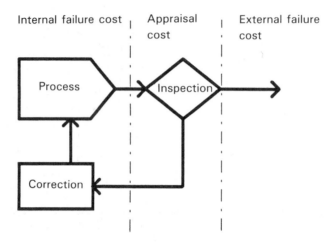

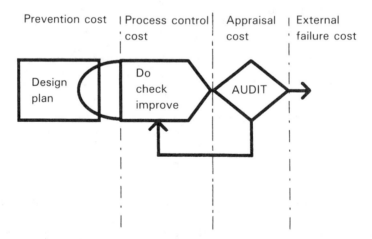

Fig. 4.5

availability of specific sensors, require major investment, and are unsuitable for destructive testing.

This does not mean that inspection itself is not useful. Inspection is essential when knowledge of the process is insufficient, for example during the early stages of product and process development. But entrusting quality responsibility to an inspection specialist means that the problem is pushed downstream, so depriving the line personnel of essential feedback. As a result, they may feel justified in taking shortcuts and relaxing discipline, relying on others to screen, sort or correct.

As it becomes more and more difficult to trace problems back to their origin, non-quality increases and accumulates at the end of the process, on the last work stations where added value is high. Clearly, quality is a line responsibility that must never be delegated to quality specialists, though they do have a role to play in assuring and auditing quality.

Shortening the feedback loop, as shown in Figure 4.5, makes it much easier for the line operators to learn and improve the process, following the four steps of the Deming wheel of progress: plan, do, check, act or improve. (See Figure 4.6.) Unfortunately, even if the line operators or front line employees accept their responsibility for organizing, executing, controlling and eventually improving their tasks, they may not be competent or sufficiently trained to do so. Or again, the process itself may not be well enough designed to be capable of giving the promised level of conformity. We should not be so carried away by our enthusiasm for front line responsibility as to forget that quality must first be built into the process, before being delegated to the operators.

When unforeseen problems occur, up to 90 per cent of the responsibility

Fig. 4.6

(according to Deming) may lie with the designers and the managers of the process, though the percentage may vary greatly according to the type of process. If the process is automated, the operator's responsibility is naturally slight; if the process interacts directly with the customer as in a service delivery, then front line responsibility is much greater. But operators and employees, when they are faced with a defect or a problem that they cannot deal with, can at least transmit the information upstream and help trace it back to its origin. This implies better integration of the process and better co-operation between staff, designers or technicians and line personnel.

In summary, the old trade-off, productivity against quality, can be resolved if quality becomes the number one priority through better knowledge and control of the process. This shift from management by result and inspection, towards management for result by process control and improvement, means that the responsibility for conformity lies mainly with the process designers and line managers. How to proceed to put this into practice? For the answer, we must return to the four steps of the Deming wheel:

- process design and planning
- process control and maintenance
- process improvement
- holding the gains and process redesign
- and then starting all over again.

These stages will now be analyzed in detail.

4.3 PLANNING AND PREVENTION: ENGINEERING QUALITY INTO THE PROCESS

By investing at the outset, it is possible to avoid the far greater costs of inspection, change and correction of the process. The purpose of this investment is as follows:

1. for a better definition of the final characteristics
2. to simplify product and process design
3. for better focusing and integration of the process
4. to make the process capable of delivering the desired result
5. to anticipate problems and make the process more robust and reliable
6. to reduce sources of confusion
7. to train employees and prepare the way for automation.

We will now take up these various points.

4.3.1 Better Definition of Final Characteristics

As we have already noted, during the first stage of any process development it is essential to define carefully the final characteristics and the acceptance levels desired. This definition is often closely related to the measuring method and the test or check procedure.

The specification of quality requirements is not a trivial problem. For example, measuring the transit time of a document through an administrative circuit requires a careful definition of input and output times. Measuring 'being late' for an airline passenger requires a clear definition of significant delays and waiting times, as perceived by the customer.

Similarly, we often merely call something a defect without defining it precisely. What is a scratch, a spot or a wrinkle? When does a noise or an impurity become a defect? Specifications and acceptance limits must be precisely defined on the basis of reproducible, communicable and operational measurements and check procedures. Unquantifiable and untestable features should be made testable by refinement or reference sample. It is precisely because they can measure what they are doing that operators are able to take action and make improvements. What gets measured gets done.

4.3.2 Simplifying Product and Process Design

Is it possible to reduce the number of parts, the amount of raw materials? Can the design be simplified? Are there useless functions that could be eliminated? Is it possible to decrease the number of operations and simplify the parts routing? All these questions are aimed at reducing waste and costs, and making the product easier to produce. They belong to an overall methodology known as value analysis. Many methods are derived from it, including 'design for assembly' (Bolwijn *et al.* 1986, p. 106). This involves the post-analysis of all stages of a process by asking three questions:

Is it possible to eliminate a given part or an operation?
What does it cost to move the part and give it the correct spatial orientation?
What does it cost to carry out the actual assembly of the part?

The result of this analysis could lead to fewer parts, shorter cycle times, fewer errors, less complex machines, and hence prepare the process for automation. Naturally, all this necessitates effective co-operation between product design, process engineering and line personnel.

4.3.3 Focusing and Integrating the Process

The division of labour leads to the breakdown of processes into specialized activities according to a large number of classifications: handlers, storeworkers, lathe operators, milling machine operators, welders, press operators, inspectors, repairworkers, each category representing a homogeneous section specializing in a specific function. This detailed breakdown is like the weft of a fabric. Unfortunately, such specialization eliminates the natural sequence of operations, the warp

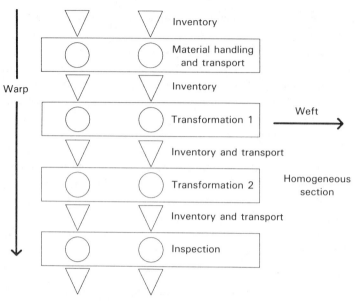

Fig. 4.7

of the fabric. (See Figure 4.7.) Although this slicing of activities like a salami by successive specialists may lead to economies of scale, the loss of process continuity makes it incompatible with quality.

To return to a coherent flow of operations that can be understood and improved, successive activities must be brought together again, and products must be regrouped into homogeneous families (group technology). This is a return to a product approach as opposed to a functional approach. Where large and complex production operations are involved, the product 'highways' or mainstreams should be identified and laid down, and existing lay-outs modified where necessary. This will provide line managers with a focused and integrated group of activities, directed towards a clear mission and visible goals.

As the course of the process flow becomes more focused and integrated, concealed non-added values and non-quality costs lodged in the interfaces between operations will become visible. Examples of such costs are materials handling, inventories, rescheduling, wasted space, data-processing, reworking, engineering changes, etc. In the flow logic that brings successive operations closer together, inventory and time lags are once again apparent. As a consequence, reaction times and production cycles can be shortened.

4.3.4 Making the Process Capable

The process should be designed in such a way that, under normal control conditions, the promised result is always obtained within acceptable variation limits.

For example, if luggage must be delivered to air passengers within a maximum waiting time of five minutes, design of the baggage delivery process and lay-out should allow for this delay each time a flight lands.

Using the experience gained from similar processes or from field work, designers should define specifications and quality levels according to the 'normal' capability of the corresponding delivery process. Zero defect or error-free work does not mean perfection. It means obtaining a result within the limits laid down by the specification, i.e. within acceptable tolerance limits.

The manufacturing of a product or the delivery of a service is a random phenomenon. The process is under control when the natural dispersion of results follows the normal distribution pattern, the well-known bell-shaped curve. In this, results are symmetrically distributed around the desired nominal value. This nominal distribution is the result of adding together many small and random causes of variations, called common causes. The process is capable when the natural dispersion of results remains well within the tolerance limits laid down by the design department. This dispersion is often referred to as noise which is analogous to the noise found in electronic signals. (See Figure 4.8.)

If a zero defect capability is to be built into the process, tolerance limits should be designed so that all production falls within them. As can be seen in Figure 4.9, when limits are set at three standard deviations from the mean, a defect rate of 1350 ppm can be expected either side of the distribution. With four standard deviations the defect rate is 30 ppm (30 chances in a million of getting it wrong).

The capability of a process is expressed by the ratio between the tolerance interval and the natural dispersion of results, often represented by three standard deviations. Thus a capability of 1, when the tolerance interval corresponds to three standard deviations, will allow 1350 defects per million, while a capability of 1.33, corresponding to four standard deviations, will allow 30 defects per million, either side. (See Figure 4.10.)

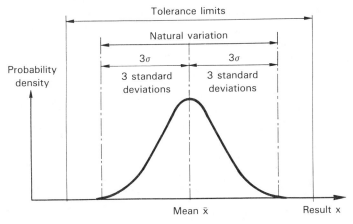

Fig. 4.8

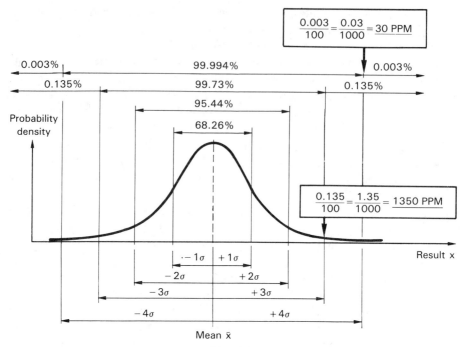

Fig. 4.9

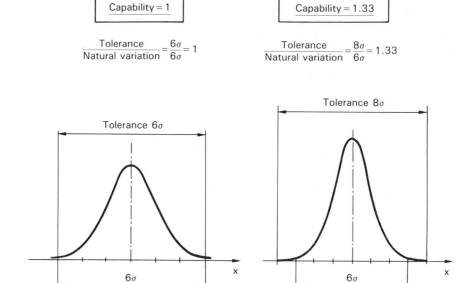

Fig. 4.10

To keep a supposedly capable process under control, the operators must regularly measure the final result by taking small samples. As soon as the result exceeds predetermined control limits, they must stop and correct the process. Thus the operators act directly on the process to prevent any drift (special causes of variation) instead of leaving it to the inspection of finished batches. However, once the process is stopped for correction they must know which parameter to adjust in order to set things right. In this way they learn more about the process and accumulate knowledge. This underlines the importance of special studies and experimental designs to make it possible to identify the essential parameters and optimal operational values.

When the process is non-repetitive or less quantifiable, capability can be established by experimentation and prototyping. In any case the result of this analysis is the definiton of check points, standards and operating procedures to control the process.

4.3.5 Anticipating Problems and Making the Process Reliable

'It is what is *not* known that kills projects' (Ould, 1990, p. 96). The identification and listing of risks can be achieved through formal project reviews, i.e. working meetings of the various parties concerned (production, maintenance, after-sales, purchasing, quality control) at which the new product or process is subjected to constructive criticism before being implemented. The group concentrates on detecting and recording errors and potential problems.

When risks are systematically explored in this way, the main problem encountered is usually the proliferation of potential failure modes, the effect of which can be more or less serious. Risks can be classified by weighing the gravity of these effects against the probability of occurrence of a given failure mode. In this respect, we can quote the FMEA method (failure mode and effect analysis). Using this, risks are systematically analyzed in order of importance, and solutions are sought by means of numerous studies and experiments. They are then implemented by means of engineering changeovers, foolproofing devices, alarms, etc.

4.3.6 Reducing Sources of Confusion and Variability

Overload, the use of equipment beyond its capacity limit, and large volume variations can both lead to failures and breakdowns. It is clear that with proper planning of the process, these problems can be overcome at source.

Confusion is another source of problems. Confusion can result from:

● multiple engineering changes applied after the poorly prepared introduction of a new product. In this case, not only will the extra costs of corrective action need to be taken into account, but also the launching delays;

- modification of the process without giving prior information or adequate training to the personnel concerned;
- poorly co-ordinated reassignment of staff (inadequate training, temporary staff, unclear procedures);
- frequent changes in the mix and the volume of production on equipment of insufficient capability or with poorly trained operators;
- insufficient maintenance of facilities: up-to-date but unreliable equipment; inadequate preventive maintenance; start-up, stoppage, wear or overload monitoring procedures that are unclear or not complied with.

4.3.7 Empowering Employees or Preparing for Automation

Establishing the capability of the process is not enough. Employees should be able to deliver the promised result right first time. In the case of 'self' inspection and control, when the process is less repetitive or less quantifiable the operators themselves are made responsible for quality. But they can only do this if they are given clear specifications and procedures, and can measure and control what they do. The process should then be reorganized to transfer ownership and improve the operators' capacity to act and learn. After all, why should people who are quite capable of repairing their own cars, managing their own budgets and calling in the appropriate specialist when work needs to be done on their houses, lose these faculties as soon as they enter the factory gates? As 'citizens/guardians of their work process' they should be capable of taking over some of the responsibilities entrusted to support departments or management, and of enriching their jobs in the following areas:

- quality control and improvement;
- organization of work place – clean and tidy;
- scheduling and material handling;
- first level preventive maintenance;
- training of colleagues.

The transfer of ownership to the team also leads to job enlargement and job rotation. The operators become multiskilled and co-operate more with each other. The supervisor becomes more of a coach and a trainer. The quality assurance inspector becomes more of a referee, who can blow the whistle when necessary.

However, 'self' inspection and control is not always applicable, and most of the time operators follow the standards and check procedures defined by process designers who bear the real responsibilities for the quality obtained. When a problem or a defect appears in the process, the first question to ask is whether standards or procedures exist. If they exist but have not been complied with, they should be revised if necessary. Standards have a limited lifetime. They should not be considered permanent, but constantly adjusted and improved. It may also be that the operators have not been adequately selected and trained. Whatever the situation, the participation of operators is essential in the adjustment of standards and procedures. The operators should not help the system perpetuate old evils; at Toyota, for example, any operator has the right to stop the line. If a requirement or a procedure is inadequate, it must be changed. Comments such as 'we have never respected that tolerance but everything works OK' are simply not acceptable.

Quality should be built into the process, but operators and line managers should have a say in the establishment of standards and procedures as they learn and improve the process. Obviously, as the process becomes more repetitive and more standardized, the participation of the line personnel will be more and more orientated towards automation with more and more learning and quality control built into the process.

4.4 CONTROL AND STABILIZATION OF THE PROCESS

Once quality has been built into the process, specifications, standards or procedures are formalized. Operators must carry out check procedures and take action to stabilize and control the process to ensure that quality requirements have been achieved.

4.4.1 Statistical Process Control

This method applies when the process is regular and repetitive and the result quantifiable. It consists in regularly taking small samples in order to measure and check the average and the dispersion of certain characteristics of the final product. The results are recorded on control charts and if they exceed acceptable limits, the process is stopped and a corrective action is taken and recorded. Parameters (raw

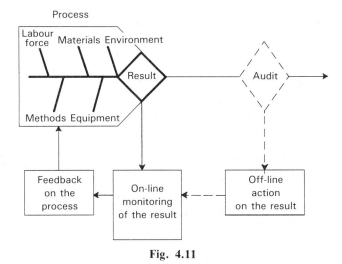

Fig. 4.11

materials, machine, method, training) which appear to be responsible are corrected. Step by step, the parameters which have the greatest influence on the process emerge, and knowledge of the process is improved. (See Figure 4.11.)

The process is said to be under control when the results are distributed according to a normal law, which always appears when many small sources of variation come together randomly. As these common causes of variation are independent and non-specific, the process remains steady and under control. However, the process is no longer under control when specific causes emerge and lead to drift or deviation.

Controlling the process therefore consists of finding and eliminating the specific problems or the sporadic parameter variations that disrupt the process. If it were possible to know and control the key parameters and factors affecting the result of the process, less or no sampling should be necessary. The control chart monitoring the final characteristics could be replaced by control charts monitoring input or intermediate factors. With this method control moves upstream, from result to causal factors. (See Figure 4.12.)

4.4.2 Process Checks and Formalization

This reasoning can be extended to any process. When you produce plastic parts on moulding presses you will check the composition of the plastic going into the hopper; you will check that the dies are correctly aligned, that the different temperatures and pressures are correct, that the time the operator takes to inspect his machine is appropriate, etc. For each of these input checks, you will have to define standards and check procedures. The final quality requirement will be achieved if all contributing factors are under control.

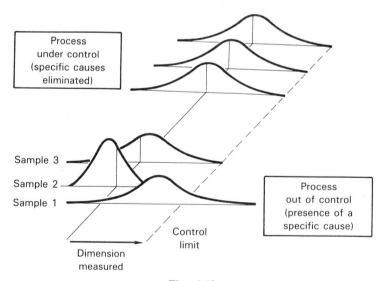

Fig. 4.12

Clearly, formalizing the process and setting standards are a good way of looking out for the onset of deviations. For example, the team leader knows that the operator takes one minute to check the five machines under his supervision. This is one of his monitoring indicators. If the team leader notes that the time taken is longer, he will analyze the reason with the operator and then do something about it. As they move upstream, measurements and standards become more physical, more concrete and more closely connected to the factors conditioning the process.

4.4.3 Standards and Procedures

Process control therefore involves standardization and measurement at all stages, which goes along with discipline and training. However, neither standards nor operating procedures are permanent. They must be regularly adjusted, updated and validated by both operators and line management who should produce operational guides for training and for the supervision of tricky points deserving special attention. Standardization paves the way for 'self' inspection on the one hand, but also for alarms, foolproofing devices and automatic controls on the other.

4.4.4 'Self' Inspection

At every stage of the process, quality control activities should establish that the required quality is achieved. Once the specifications and the check procedures have been defined, the operator can carry out the check, record the result or make sure any corrective action is taken. The operator can only be made responsible for the quality of his output if he has been trained and the process is capable, if he is given valid standards and procedures, if he can measure what he is doing and eventually take corrective action. These constraints apply even if the process is less repetitive, the result more customized or less quantifiable (assembly line, service delivery). In this last case, jobs and activities can be enlarged to end up in a more meaningful and complete or task 'deliverable'.

As we have seen, the line managers become less involved in direct supervision and act more as advisers, method specialists and trainers. They set up the relevant indicators and standards that will provide early warning of the need for process maintenance and improvement.

4.4.5 Foolproofing the Process

The human operator is fallible, so to minimize the influence of human error various methods have been developed:

— aids to operators (fixtures, sense magnifiers, etc.);
— automated tests (fail safe devices, alarms, cut-offs, etc.);
— countdowns and checklists.

Foolproofing operations is very popular in Japan under the name of poka-yoke (Shingo, 1986). It often results from the implementation of the solution to a problem tackled by a quality circle.

4.5 IMPROVEMENT AND HOLDING ON TO THE GAINS

A standard is not a once-for-all reference; it should evolve. As Masaiki Imai said during one of his seminars, if your work has not changed in two years, then you have no grounds for asking for a salary increase! A manager should not be assessed solely on the accomplishment and control of his assigned objectives, but also on the progress achieved. Large step changes introduced by staff specialists to 'rationalize' the process and accommodate new technologies are necessary but not sufficient by themselves. The quality levels aimed for can only be achieved if continuous improvement takes place between each of these large steps. A large reorganization represents a 'bulldozer' approach to quality and productivity gains, while working with a 'plane', slice after slice, is the continuous improvement approach.

4.5.1 Reducing Variation

The elimination of specific causes of variation leaves the process once more under control, but why stop there? Why not try to reduce variation further, gain more capability and make the process even more robust? (See Figure 4.13.)

In practice, however, the system is not organized to make this investment possible. Given time and money constraints, the initial capability of the process will tend to persist over time.

4.5.2 Correcting Sporadic Problems

At the outset, then, the process provides an acceptable quality level to which all concerned adapt. As the process designers will already have started work on another project, most of the corrective effort will be aimed at maintaining the status quo. If sporadic deviation occurs, operators and management will intervene to restore the situation. Should a more serious problem or crisis crop up, an *ad hoc* team of 'fire fighters' will be formed to bring the system back to normal. For most of the time, the fire fighters will rely on their own resourcefulness and palliative solutions.

4.5.3 Continuing, In-depth Improvement

Improving a process implies a genuine attempt to reduce the chronic, acceptable level of poor quality. This involves a refusal to accept mediocrity, and a commitment to invest in specific improvement projects. For example, a manufacturer of aluminium foil that is destined for photography has not only to attain zero defects

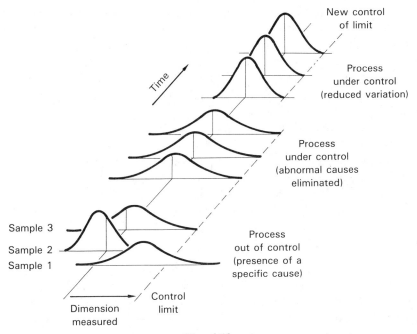

Fig. 4.13

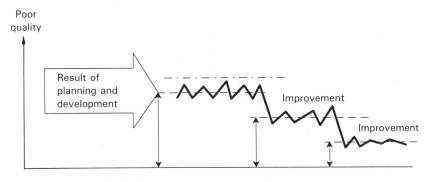

Project-by-project improvement

Fig. 4.14

within tolerances, the tolerances themselves must be constantly adjusted and reduced as the defects become increasingly microscopic and visual inspection alone no longer satisfies the customer. (See Figure 4.14.)

How to Clear the Fog by Measurement

How are we to select improvement projects? The essential thing is to make malfunctions, waste and defects visible, and clear the 'fog' enveloping the process, as this fog or 'noise' reduces our ability to learn. Measurements and indicators must be implemented to identify where the improvement efforts should be concentrated. One possibility is by using the well-known cost of quality concept, but this is a lagging indicator which appears after the facts. However, measuring the cost of quality necessitates setting up a specific enquiry to find out hidden problems or non-added values concealed in or between the processes. It is often simpler and more effective to use physical indicators that are concrete and directly linked to the process, such as delays, defects, inventories, downtimes, etc.

Once the indicators have been selected, deviations and problems have to be located and dealt with one by one. This is rather like clearing away stones or boulders as they emerge above the surface of the water, in order to make a river navigable. Inspection, remember, acts like a downstream dam, enabling the water to reach a level that will conceal the boulders and the problems and making them impossible to locate. How can the river be cleared? Several methods are possible, among them these three:

1. Empty the river completely by diverting it, and so enable every problem to be reviewed and counted. This is an ambitious programme, often termed 'reorganization' or 'rationalization', the sort of programme undertaken by engineering and support departments. These are our large steps hewn out by a bulldozer. It is a radical but rather illusory method, especially if the environment is dynamic and complex. An incremental approach may be preferable. (See Figure 4.15.)
2. Gradually lower the water level while carefully watching the surface, and then remove the boulders one by one, project by project, as they emerge. By beginning with the most troublesome and clearly visible blocks, managers and the staff responsible for the process, organized into quality improvement teams, should be able to deal in priority with these 'vital few' problems, in order to improve the overall 'navigability' of the process.

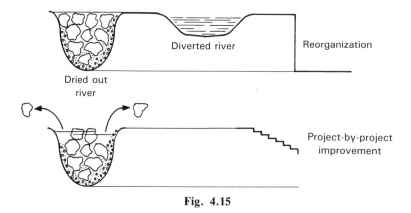

Fig. 4.15

3. Clear the sand and the pebbles, thus resolving the host of minor problems strewn on the bottom and the banks of the river. This is a simpler task which can be entrusted to the operators, organized into quality circles, or process quality improvement teams.

In the two last cases the process is improved on-line using the natural data.

The Method: Diagnosis and Remedy

As we shall see in Chapter 11, the method used to solve problems is an experimental one, encouraging group creativity and involving the classical steps: definition and analysis of the situation, diagnosis, choice and implementation of a solution, and the recording and standardization of the knowledge thus obtained.

Holding on to the Gains

Once a problem has been resolved, the organization must ensure that the solution is memorized to prevent the same situation from recurring. This again involves learning and the integration of this new knowledge into procedures, training or any mechanism designed to prevent the repetition of past errors. This experimental knowledge can be recorded either in the process itself (automatic mechanism, foolproofing), in the operating documents (log book, quality manuals, control sheets) or in the minds of the operators (procedures, training).

This is a long-haul operation and the basis of real cultural change. As a well-known maxim puts it, 'Those who cannot remember the past are condemned to repeat it.'

4.5.4 Reducing Non-added Values

The continuous improvement approach to quality we have just discussed can be extended to all sorts of wastage and non-added values. In fact, when analyzing a process it is possible to distinguish between useful activities (leading to added value, i.e. technological transformation) and other activities which do not bring direct added value, even though they are sometimes necessary. (See Figure 4.16.)

The same project-by-project, continuous improvement approach applies when dealing with inventories, lead times, material handling and transportation, data-processing, set-up and adjustment costs or breakdowns, etc. Total quality can be combined with total maintenance (total productive maintenance) to prepare for the next stage, the stockless, just-in-time flow management.

As production runs grow longer, flows become more regular and can be pulled from downstream. As set-up times are reduced, batch sizes and work in process inventories decrease, flows are tightened and the production cycle is shortened. The process is capable of delivering large volumes, while accepting a more flexible

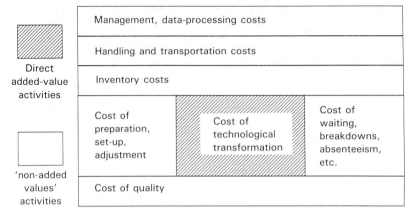

Fig. 4.16

mix of products. Total quality prepares the ground for the next battle, the battle for flexibility.

To conclude, let us say that quality leads to productivity and paves the way for flexibility.

CHAPTER 5

•

QUALITY AS AN ECONOMIC AND SOCIAL SOLUTION: CONTROLLING AND IMPROVING THE SYSTEM

Chapter 4 showed how a better knowledge of the process, and individual participation in prevention, control and improvement can lead on to quality of conformity and hence essential productivity gains. This chapter will extend that method to the rest of the organization, to the corporate system as a whole. We will remain within the framework of the first reform which aimed at conformity, the total assurance that the customer will receive a result corresponding to the contract agreed, i.e. error-free work from the outset.

At the corporate level making quality a top priority remains an internal solution which is first of all economic, thanks to prevention, control and improvement, and secondly social, in that solidarity is restored.

Total quality then develops along two axes: the natural vertical direction within the function or department, and the cross-functional or interdepartmental direction. (See Figure 5.1.) We shall be analyzing:

1. Total quality in each function and department ('A' in Figure 5.1);
2. Total quality across functions, breaking down the barriers ('B' in Figure 5.1).

5.1 TOTAL QUALITY IN EACH FUNCTION AND DEPARTMENT

5.1.1 Management Responsibility for Quality

The corporate system is made up of a set of functions and departments which contribute to the chain of added values, beginning with design and ending with the sales or after-sales service. Each function, be it design, purchasing, industrial engineering or manufacturing, comprises a certain number of processes. The approach developed in the previous chapter can be extended to encompass them all.

If quality of conformity is to become or remain a top priority for everyone concerned, it is essential that each and every manager of the function or department concerned accept it as their basic responsibility. This responsibility cannot be delegated to quality control specialists, management must set an example. Managers are responsible for the maintenance and improvement of their system. They must

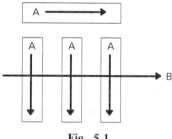

Fig. 5.1

ascertain that every process and every operator is capable of error-free work. If a single part of the chain is at all lacking, the end result will be affected, as probabilities of success multiply from step to step.

The maintenance and stabilization of the system, therefore, requires that the standards and procedures, defined and revised with the participation of all concerned, are resolutely followed and complied with. The task of management here is not so much to supervise and meticulously inspect the application of a host of rules and orders, as to identify and follow a small number of essential indicators that show how the system is actually functioning. The role of management is to know, understand and work on its system in order to pinpoint the small number of truly decisive indicators. For example, the results of a salesperson depend on the number of effective calls made (the right person, present and available) and not the time spent in the office or in bureaucratic inspection of administrative work. A good monitoring system does not contain all twenty-five variables identified, but the three most relevant that condition the results. Should there be any deviation, management must know which variables should be adjusted to achieve the required result (additional resources, training, etc.).

Once again, the role of management is not so much to maintain the status quo as to anticipate and help everyone better to control his or her individual contribution. The guidelines are there to enable a diagnosis of the situation and the identification of problematic areas where efforts should be focused in order to build quality into the system.

The better its control over the system, the more ambitious management can be in setting its targets. It will be much more inclined to demand a 50 per cent error reduction or a 30 per cent decrease in the production cycle if these objectives can be expressed in what Juran refers to as 'the language of things'. Juran says that a manager should be bilingual, and speak the language of money as well as the language of things. Asking for a 10 per cent cost réduction is speaking only the language of money, a language that is too simplistic. It could be interpreted as saying, 'I want my 10 per cent cost reduction, I don't know the system but just you get on with it and do your best.' By contrast, knowing the system well enough to be able to identify sensitive variables and potential improvements is really and truly managing and engineering progress. The 10 per cent cost reduction will inevitably appear on the bottom line as a consequence.

In every function and department, therefore, managers must take the lead with regard to quality and inspire their personnel to follow them, possibly with the aid of a facilitator at the outset. The method followed will always be the same: prevent and plan, control and standardize, diagnose and improve, project by project.

The first step to improvement is a diagnosis of the current situation in order to identify and outline projects of interest. We are not talking about a comprehensive and systematic analysis of the system, but a surface diagnosis to get the process under way. This is the most difficult and sensitive area, and demands the most of management. After this, teams are set up and given selected projects, to be dealt with by the conventional experimental method (definition of problem, investigation of causes, search for a solution, implementation, learning).

Once the few vital problems are on the way to being resolved, the host of minor local problems can be dealt with by quality circles or quality improvement teams. This sequence corresponds to removing the pebbles and sand from the bed and banks of the river after clearing away the boulders preventing the normal course of operations. Clearly the solving of these local problems by means of such group activity can only be undertaken within the framework of a larger movement to solve the major problems. After all, you don't sweep a staircase from the bottom upwards.

5.1.2   The Next Process is also a Customer

In most cases any error will have an effect on the next process. People are particularly inclined to pass the buck to a neighbour when that neighbour is a long way off, or just a vague acquaintance. But if instead we consider him as a customer, we stress the importance of controlling each stage before going on to the following one. The customer who complains is then helping the supplier's process, by telling him what needs correcting.

Once again, the role of management is to work on the system to restore solidarity, the cement that links the various sub-systems. It is not so much a question of changing attitudes as modifying the organization so as to reduce distance barriers or inventories. Changes of attitude will then follow naturally. If, between the customer and the supplier of parts, there is half an hour's inventory instead of three days' production, information concerning an assembly defect will be more relevant and more effective. By better understanding his customer's problems, the internal supplier will learn how to control and improve his own process.

We should note that the customer–supplier relationship becomes even more important between two separate functions or departments. We will be returning to this subject at greater length in section 5.2.

5.1.3   The Role of the Quality Assurance or Quality Control Department

What role remains for a quality assurance department to play if everyone is responsible for his or her own work?

Quality Assurance

Quality assurance is responsible for formally expressing quality objectives through the establishment of a quality management system to check that predetermined quality control activities are properly executed. Its role is to assure and reassure customers that specifications and promises have been and will be complied with, according to the accepted operating standards where they exist. This is not an operational but an auditing role.

Quality assurance is there to maintain the 'tables of the law', to structure know-how and procedures intelligently and concretely. It is not merely a registry accumulating successive layers of procedures and constraints, but a proactive structured system with certification, standards, procedures and know-how plans. It is the guardian of the law, but at the same time it should not lose contact with the real world, nor should it multiply regulations without first pruning the old ones. Regulations must be integrated into a coherent whole. The law must be nourished by everyday practice, and that practice recorded in the form of laws.

Contributing Methods, Advice and Training

Quality assurance should help other functions to progress by providing a means of measurement and proven methods (statistics, reliability, experimental designs). To avoid the danger of becoming bureaucratic, its members, who will be well trained and familiar with concepts and tools, should operate in other departments as trainers and consultants.

Gathering Information and Co-ordinating Feedback

The role of quality assurance is similar to that of management control, but whereas a management audit measures financial deviations versus the budget, quality assurance looks at conformity deviations and failures to comply with standards. These deviations may appear not only in individual departments, but also throughout the entire organization, from product definition to after-sales and even guarantees, not forgetting complaints, documentation and training.

If it is to be helpful, information must be extremely detailed, precise and concrete and provided in this form very quickly, while problems are being filtered out according to their degree of seriousness.

The Quality Management System

A great deal of work has been done in industry in defining what constitutes a quality management system, and this has resulted in national and international standards, for example, ISO9001 or equivalent standards in different industries (defence, nuclear, etc.). The effectiveness of these standards comes from the existence of bodies able to give an accreditation, that is to certify that the quality management system of a given firm conforms to the standard.

5.2 TOTAL QUALITY ACROSS FUNCTIONS – BREAKING DOWN THE BARRIERS

A total quality policy aimed at conformity and zero defects has the major advantage of being easy to explain, understand or to extend throughout the organization. However, it is particularly difficult to implement, as it requires co-operation between departments and functions. These have an unfortunate tendency to develop their own cultures and objectives and to neglect malfunctions or problems outside their own department. However, the very concept of system and organization implies solidarity of its component parts *vis-à-vis* a common objective. In its first meaning, total quality is aimed at every department from top to bottom. In its second meaning, it is systemic and crosses the organization horizontally. This co-operative policy requires powerful and committed management, capable of forcing departments out of their ivory towers and returning to the customer–supplier dialogue, either by cross-functional improvement groups, by team work to develop new products, or by partnership with outside suppliers.

5.2.1 Cross-functional Customer–Supplier Relationships

The customer–supplier relationship between two departments is an excellent instance of the dual aspect already stressed in our definition of quality: the right product and the product right, the right service and the service right, efficiency and effectiveness.

Let us take the simple example of a training department preparing a seminar for the sales department. The training department is the supplier of the sales department, which is its customer. The internal customer–supplier relationship is characterized by a service which must not only be well performed but must also be effective, i.e. enable the sales force to increase its sales. (See Figure 5.2.)

Controlling this relationship therefore involves a value analysis phase of customer requirements, before tackling conformity. Though obvious, this fact tends to be gradually forgotten as the system becomes more and more routine. Departments and sub-systems communicate less and less because their work is organized by rules and standards. Besides, they do not have the time to question

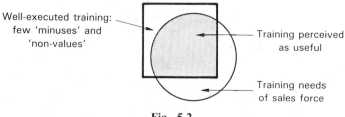

Well-executed training: few 'minuses' and 'non-values'

Training perceived as useful

Training needs of sales force

Fig. 5.2

customers. The natural tendency of every service is to think in terms of its own square, as each one of us tends to think according to the type of seat we are sitting on. The end result is that measurement of results is conducted according to criteria internal to the supplier department, not that of the customer department. This soon leads to the creation of a comprehension barrier between the departments concerned.

We are very familiar with the wall separating the design department from the production department, where the new, finished product file is tossed over the wall dividing the two departments. Such a division is due to differences in language, culture, vision, and frequently geographical separation. Sometimes the other department is considered as the enemy, which makes the idea of consultation akin to spying. Here we are in the sensitive world of co-operative strategies in organizational sociology, which we will come back to later. What are the characteristics of the customer–supplier relationship?

The Relationship is Dynamic Involving Direct Adjustment in Both Directions

- The customer explains and simplifies his needs. He informs his supplier as soon as possible of any problem or changes (which he minimizes).
- The supplier does not necessarily accept all the customer's requests. His response is based on his own resources and constraints, though he maintains a certain capacity for adjustment to changes. He will take these changes into consideration as soon as possible. However, he must give 100 per cent of what he has promised and assume responsibility for it. (See Figure 5.3.)

Direct communication means less recourse to the chain of command and staff departments. The supplier is able to understand and adapt directly to his customer on the basis of the actual situation. This law of the situation is less binding than the law of authority imposed from above.

Control of the Relationship in Accordance with Customer Assessment and Criteria

By expressing his needs directly, the customer defines the terms of the contract in accordance with his own criteria and checks the result according to his own

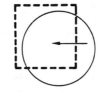

Needs or requirements

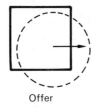

Offer

Fig. 5.3

assessment and perception. The supplier can no longer promise one thing and deliver another, since evaluation and inspection are carried out by the customer on his own terms. For example, measurement of a delay takes account of all the delays perceived by the customer, not just production time.

Improvement by Better Adjustment and Reduction of Malfunctions

Improved adjustment and error reduction are not systematically taken into account by the traditional organization. They can, however, be covered by value analysis groups or improvement groups working with specific methods.

Value Analysis Teams
Are the needs of a given customer department covered by the activities of the supplier department? This functional analysis is performed in four stages:

Analysis phase: Why?
Analysis of functions really necessary for the customer: major and secondary functions (expressed by a verb and a noun); effectiveness measurement as seen by the client.

Analysis phase: How?
Analysis of operations supplied. Role of each activity? How much does it cost, could it be eliminated?

Creativity phase: alternatives, opportunities
Could each activity be done differently, could it be more effective or more efficient?

Implementation phase
Change and reorganization proposals, implementation problems.

As an example, Figure 5.4 is a functional analysis matrix of the communication

Essential purpose	Basic functions	Primary activities							
		Edit publications	Prepare audiovisuals	Design brochures	Promote contests	Train staff	Automate systems	Etc.
Support sales	Communicate information	X	X	X				
	Develop sales support		X	X				
	Provide recognition				X			
	Manage function					X		
Support	Satisfy user					X		
	Assure dependability						X	

Need → How? → Why?

Corporate communication

Source: Paul Revere Insurance Company (B) (1981), HBS Case 9-687-033 exhibit 1, p. 14.

Fig. 5.4

service of the Paul Revere Insurance Company. (Paul Revere Insurance Company 1981). Two of the activities here are editing publications and promoting contests.

By asking the question why or what is the purpose of an activity such as 'design sales brochures', we can trace it back to the source function: 'communicate information' or 'develop sales support'. The question, 'Why is this function necessary?' helps identify the essential function 'support sales'. By this means it is possible to go from activities to basic functions, and then right up to the essential purpose of the department. Each activity can be classified according to its importance for the customer, its quality of conformity and its cost. Clearly an activity to which there is no answer to the Why question should be dropped. Conversely, the question 'How should this function be realized?' leads to existing activities, their transformation or new activities.

Implemented at regular intervals by staff and management teams, this method can result in far-reaching organizational changes and improvements.

Quality Improvement Teams

Quality improvement involves measuring and analyzing malfunctions which have crept into client–supplier relationships, just like the boulders on the river bed which hamper the regular flow of the water. The non-quality problems of interest here are problems which emerge chronically. They have come to stay, and must be fiercely attacked with scientific and objective methodology if they are to be rooted out once and for all.

5.2.2 Improvement of Cross-functional Processes

The previous improvement approach may be extended to cross-functional processes covering several interfaces. Thus, the voice of the customer is transmitted horizontally from department to department, or from the front office to the back office, causing each activity to be adjusted to the needs of its internal customer. (See Figure 5.5.)

Quality can only be maintained if there is a dialogue, if the contract between the parties concerned is clear and regularly updated, for this will inevitably facilitate the faultless execution of the contract. The transmission of customer needs throughout the system means spelling out the main sub-objectives at each and every customer–supplier interface.

When for example SAS (Scandinavian Airlines System) decided to focus its efforts on flight punctuality for the Euroclass segment, the objective handed down to the luggage handlers was quite clear: 'Luggage must be on the carousel when passengers arrive to pick it up.' Once the main objective is defined, the rest follows naturally. Fewer standards and procedures are then necessary.

Invoicing is another example of a cross-functional process with many customer–supplier interfaces. It begins with order taking, goes to the plant, passes through the logistics services, returns to accounts, and then comes back to the

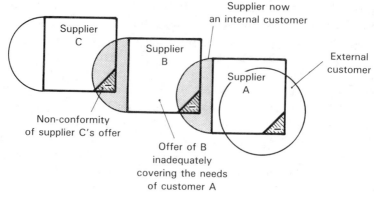

Supplier now
an internal customer

External
customer

Non-conformity
of supplier C's offer

Offer of B
inadequately
covering the needs
of customer A

Fig. 5.5

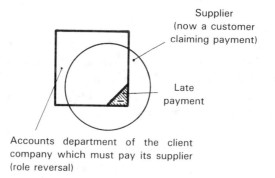

Supplier
(now a customer
claiming payment)

Late
payment

Accounts department of the client
company which must pay its supplier
(role reversal)

Fig. 5.6

client. Modifications may be added along the way, and the final record of all these movements will end up in a data bank on computer. The result may be an impressive level of errors due to the large number of operators and operations involved. Once again the probability of success is a product of probabilities.

Let us take another, slightly more complex example: the supplier of a corporation complains to accounts that payments are late. In this case the supplier becomes the customer of the corporate accounts department. (See Figure 5.6.) But the reason for delay is upstream of the accounts department: the reception department makes mistakes – badly filled-in forms, poor knowledge of reception procedures, etc. (See Figure 5.7.)

The method for improving these cross-functional processes consists in making them visible by describing them, defining them and appointing a responsible owner. The owner may be a single person or a multifunctional group, but whoever it is, it will design the flow of operations, define measurement of the result and check points on the process itself. It will then proceed according to the traditional 'plan, do, check, act' of the Deming wheel, that is to say audit, improvement, reorganization and implementation and again, audit, improvement, and so on.

Two-faced Janus

Whichever department is concerned, and whether it is interacting with an external or an internal customer, it will be coping with two aspects. The first is an efficiency approach, which goes up the hierarchical line and covers productivity, control of resources and expenses. This approach remains within the square logic. The second is an effectiveness approach which is based on adaptation to customer satisfaction. This is an integrative approach directed towards the final circle, the customer. (See Figure 5.8.)

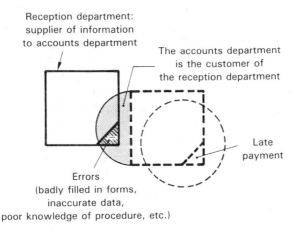

Fig. 5.7

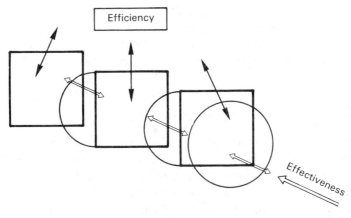

Fig. 5.8

5.2.3 A Special Type of Cross-functional Process — The Development of a New Product

Non-qualities appear mainly during and after production. The operators, however, only control a small portion of the defects. Their responsibility ranges from 5 per cent to 20 per cent (according to the level of customization and the type of industry), which is relatively low. Conformity of the result depends on the generating process, involving managers and engineers responsible for defining, designing or engineering. Their task is to build quality into the system so that the operators will, under normal conditions, be in a position to achieve zero defects.

Let us take, for example, an instrument with an attachment lug which breaks during assembly. The questions which should be put when attempting to solve this problem are: is the lug really useful, is there a design fault (inadequate thickness, brittle material) or is it a case of non-conformity? If so, is this non-conformity due to a poorly designed process (displacement of both parts of the mould when casting the part) or to a production error (setting error on the machine)? (See Figure 5.9.)

The further the sequence prevention, control and improvement is implemented, the more we find that responsibility moves back from the defect observed by the customer to quality control, from quality control to production, from production to industrial engineering, from engineering to design, and from design to definition of the offer. At the same time, the dialogue between these various departments is reinforced.

It is important to make a clear distinction between the various stages of product development and the various departments or services involved in the project. It becomes less and less acceptable to see the different departments working in slices, one after the other, or passing the baton as in a relay race, for if they do so, they will generate mountains of engineering changes during the final stages. The principle of prevention requires systematic co-operation and linkages to anticipate problems, just as in a rugby match.

A matrix display provides a visual representation of the process and enables the preparation of a quality plan to check and foolproof the process. (See Figure 5.10.) The quality plan describes the quality control procedures and actions to check that the quality features and levels expected have been achieved and recorded at each stage.

Project Management

Managing the launching of a new product is the same as managing a new project. It is therefore essential to appoint a project manager, a steering group or a co-ordination committee. The strengthening of cross-functional links between services and departments can be further intensified by planning a number of meetings at the appropriate times, so that potential problems may be anticipated as early as possible.

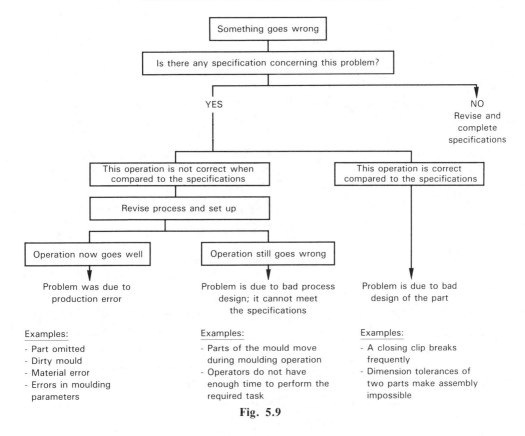

Fig. 5.9

Prevention by Project Reviews

The aim of project reviews, also known as design reviews, synthesis groups or development conferences, is to submit the project, once it has reached a specific degree of development, to the critical and constructive analysis of all functions concerned. As a result, the project can be simplified, and outstanding technical issues and potential problems highlighted and resolved before drawings, specifications or processes are fixed.

Some design changes can facilitate production. It may even be that some specifications required by the design department have not been requested by the customer. For example, by eliminating screws and springs a printer manufacturer considerably simplified both the industrial process and assembly, while at the same time reducing in-service problems. 'Swatch' watches are never repaired; there are no spare parts. This commercial advantage and the simplification of after-sales were made possible by the greater reliability of both the product and production processes.

Another advantage of project reviews is that results can be validated, discrepancies measured and additional studies launched, at an early stage. The

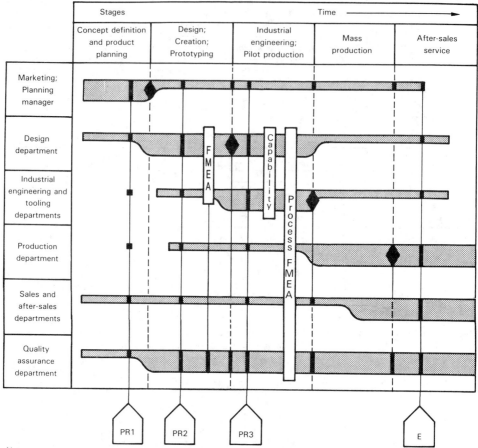

Notes

PR1 = Project review 1 = Review of product definition and reliability
PR2 = Project review 2 = Review of drawings and prototypes, reliability
PR3 = Project review 3 = Project review to prepare mass production
E   = Final evaluation and future preventive actions
♦ Verification or certification: intermediate examination when passing from one stage to the next
Capability: design should take account of machine and process capability (controlled normal variation)
FMEA: failure mode and effect analysis or any other method for potential problems analysis

Fig. 5.10

reduction of certain levels of defects or the improvement of reliability can thus be monitored step by step.

Note that project reviews and programme monitoring or progress reviews are not the same thing. The objective of progress reviews is to ensure the adequacy of planning and resources.

Prevention by FMEA Cross-functional Groups, Value Analysis...

Some cross-functional groups which use more formal methods also form part of the quality plan. Examples of these are value analysis groups, design for assembly groups (simplification of assembly by the engineering design department) or FMEA (failure mode and effect analysis) groups (see Figure 5.10).

The FMEA method is used both at the design stage – FMEA product – and at the engineering stage – FMEA process. When exploring potential problems, the difficulty lies in the proliferation of possible failure modes that must be considered. The method is therefore initially focused on the classification of failure modes by scoring the seriousness of the effect on the client, on a scale of 1 to 10. This score is then weighted by the probability of occurrence of this failure mode (again on a scale from 1 to 10) and the probability of its non-detection (on a similar scale).

Once the problems have been classified and ranked according to their score, they can then be worked on and eliminated by determining their causes and validating the solution proposed by testing, calculation and systematic plans of experiments. It is essential to plan this elimination by specific contracts where those responsible are named, and therefore know exactly what is to be done and when.

Control by Verification, Validation and Certification of the Various Phases

One of the most delicate tasks of the project leader is to break the project down into distinct, relatively independent activities. For each activity there should be a validation or a verification procedure by the manager responsible, who will set up the necessary test facilities to ensure that results are in conformity with the objectives.

Some authors like M. Ould (1990, p. 123) make the following distinction between verification and validation: verification is checking that we have built the thing right (formal proof of conformance by inspection and test); validation is checking that we have built the right thing (in the mind of the user, even if some aspects might not have been expressed).

Certification, which is conducted by quality assurance, consists of ensuring again by an independent body that the procedures and results are in conformity with requirements and standards. These independent audits or official tests are like intermediate exams. Quality assurance plays the role of 'guardian' of the process by checking and updating procedures, standards and methods.

Improvement and Updating

This high investment in prevention, planning and validation does not absolve the project manager from constantly improving and updating as information from the field (sales reports and customer surveys) reaches him. The most detailed information should be sent to those responsible as soon as possible. Assuming that the project involves four main phases: concept definition/product planning, design, industrial engineering and mass production, the project quality plan facilitates the passage from situation I to situation II, as shown in Figure 5.11. The reduction in the number of problems encountered during pilot runs and mass production can

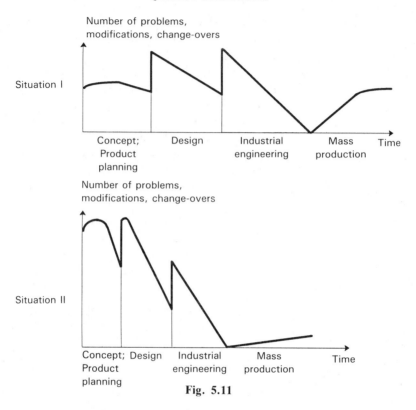

Fig. 5.11

lead to a substantial reduction in development time and cost, as there may be a huge ratio between the cost of an error eliminated at the design phase, and the same error corrected after final inspection.

Improvement of the Development Process itself

As with any project, once it has been completed, it is important to learn from any delays, overruns and unforeseen modifications that have occurred, and to improve the quality plan and the development process itself. Like any other process, it should be replanned, checked and improved.

5.2.4 Controlling Relations with External Suppliers

For simplicity's sake, the line corresponding to suppliers was omitted in the new product development quality plan (Figure 5.10). However, external purchasing represents an increasingly substantial portion of the cost of products or services. In the chemical processing industries, for example, it may represent as much as 70 per cent to 80 per cent of production costs, whereas in the automobile industry the figure is around 60 per cent. The hoped-for gains deriving from so-called vertical integration (in actual fact horizontal integration) tend to fade away in fast-changing environments. It is often easier to adjust to lower prices by subcontracting and using outside suppliers, than by dealing on with in-house suppliers on a 'privileged' basis that omits the competitive element.

Because they cover half the production costs, outside supplies represent a substantial source of non-quality which, as it permeates the chain of added values, can lead to increasingly substantial damage. Studies carried out in firms manufacturing electronic equipment show an exponential growth of costs between a defective component stopped at the outset, and a failure identified in the field. (See Figure 5.12.)

When the exponential costs of correcting poor quality are added to the purchasing price of the component, they can represent up to an extra 20 per cent or more. Therefore, it is far better to pay a 20 per cent bonus to a good supplier initially, than to seek the lowest possible price and pay for later corrections of poor quality. During negotiations, the purchaser can no longer use price and delivery time as the sole bases for judging the acceptability of the contract. He must step outside the formal contractual relationship with its final or incoming acceptance inspections, and adopt a far more in-depth form of co-operation.

Evolution of Relationship with Outside Suppliers

Arm's Length Relationship and Dual Inspection

The short-term approach of division of labour and productivity gains can lead to multiple suppliers competing against each other in an atmosphere of distrust, heightened by final inspection on the supplier's premises, and incoming inspection when the goods are delivered. This arm's length relationship is 'dry', formalized by written contracts and the exchange of papers. (See Figure 5.13.)

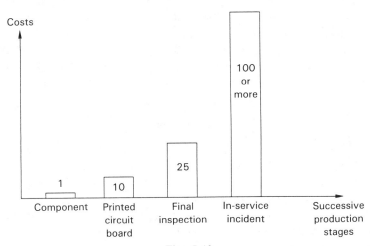

Fig. 5.12

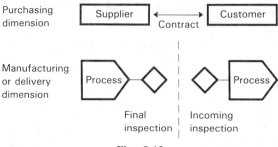

Fig. 5.13

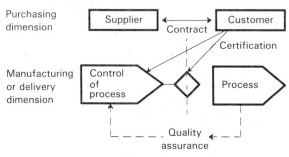

Fig. 5.14

A closer relationship involves first the elimination of incoming inspection on the customer's premises. This is superseded by inspectors visiting the supplier and auditing his inspection methods.

The Supplier Controls his Production
Final inspection of the supplier is gradually reduced as responsibility for quality is handed back to production, which endeavours to control its processes directly rather than inspect and correct its results. (See Figure 5.14.) To be accepted, the supplier must prove he is capable of producing in conformity with zero defects. Quality assurance gives added assurance to the customer with the establishment of a quality management system.

Certification of Supplier and Partnership
In the longer term, the supplier should be capable of planning quality from the design stage onwards, and extending his improvement programmes to cover all sectors. He will then be well on the way towards total quality. (See Figure 5.15.)

In the classical scenario, the producer has many suppliers competing on price and keeps them at arm's length. Partnership, on the other hand, is based on a special relationship with a single supplier or a preferred few suppliers, and long-term co-operation on a fluid, interactive basis. Partnership means less paper but more communication; open books, open orders, joint responsibility and a relationship

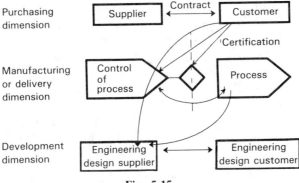

Fig. 5.15

based on trust. However, it also signifies stringent selection and rigorous 'certification' or 'accreditation' before a supplier can be placed on that privileged short list. Certification of suppliers is part of an approach summarized below, which represents the quality assurance plan to be adopted by suppliers to Rank Xerox:

Prevention at design stage
— Involvement of supplier at design stage
— Review of plans and specifications
— Development of product quality plan
— Evaluation of samples.

Process
— Study of process reproducibility – capabilities
— Characteristics to be controlled
— Finalization of quality plan.

Production
— Process control
— Final inspection and packaging.

It is clear that a change to partnership means cutting back the number of suppliers, even if it is not always necessary to go as far as Rank Xerox which, between 1981 and 1982, reduced the number of its suppliers from 4000 to 400.

The Domains of Co-operation

There are three areas:

Quality of Conformity (Objective: Zero Defect)
Simplification of product and of process, reduction of disruptions, control and improvement of process.

Technical Co-operation

The supplier is the expert. He, therefore, should be committed and quality planned from the onset of design. For its part, the design department should use standard components rather than reinventing the wheel, and endeavour to integrate better the specific constraints of suppliers.

Logistics co-operation

Clearly, co-operation can be extended to encompass the management of flows between supplier and customer. By providing early, comprehensive information, inventory can be reduced. By smoothing programmes, just-in-time can be achieved. By understanding how materials and components are used, linkages improving quality and reducing costs can be found. For example, a chocolate supplier can substantially reduce his own transport and packaging costs, as well as those of his customer, by delivering melted chocolate directly in heated trucks rather than in bars wrapped in aluminium foil.

This involves dual motion (see Figure 5.16):

● *from customer (here the purchaser) to supplier.* The customer should involve the supplier in the definition of his needs as early as possible. He should also inform the supplier very early of any changes (reduced to a minimum) or problems.

● *from supplier to customer (in this case the purchaser).* The supplier must remain flexible, but also needs to interrogate, better understand and possibly influence his customer. He should not accept everything and anything and should know where to draw the line. But once the requirements are accepted, he should give 100 per cent of the promise.

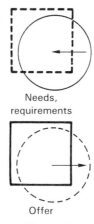

Needs,
requirements

Offer

Fig. 5.16

CHAPTER 6

•

QUALITY AS AN ECONOMIC AND SOCIAL SOLUTION: INTERNAL TURNAROUND STRATEGY AND CONDITIONS GOVERNING CHANGE

Total quality does not negate cost reduction and productivity, but precedes and implies them. By making both conformity to requirements and error-free work a priority, total quality sets in motion the first reform. This aims at the elimination of defects and waste in each process and in the entire corporate system. As stressed in Chapter 1, for many Japanese firms in the 1950s total quality began as a means of catching up with the West and overcoming their lack of competitiveness. Since then, however, the situation has been reversed, so that today, the quality movement has become a means of survival for a large number of Western corporations. Their first reactions were necessarily defensive. Internal consolidation was required before they could attempt to beat this new competition. They had to clean up their own back yard and thereby prepare, control and improve each process and hence the overall system. At this stage, conformity with requirements and zero defects are the necessary conditions to remaining in line with the competition, to surviving and staying in the game.

It should be pointed out, however, that the absence of any 'minus' can be considered as a 'plus' if the competition's quality of conformance is less than optimum. Marketing a reliable conventional product with no defect, exactly as promised and at an attractive price, can make all the difference. This strategy, initially adopted by the Japanese, was all the more efficient and incursive, given the slow reactions of the West.

In this chapter we will analyze how to turn the organization round in order to achieve conformance. After that we shall see how to capitalize on this internal strategy to prepare for the second reform: turning quality into a strategic weapon and a competitive edge. The first reform, even if it only remains internal, nevertheless represents a far-reaching transformation of the organization. Quality is no longer a problem delegated to the quality assurance department but a vector of change, a management system, a cultural model used to turn the situation around. We shall organize our analysis along two main lines:

1. Management of change and leadership.
2. Key elements of the change process.

6.1 MANAGEMENT OF CHANGE AND LEADERSHIP

Managing for quality rather than by costs and volumes represents a radical cultural change involving every process and every department from design to after-sales service, both vertically and horizontally. This kind of change can only be set in motion when a real awareness and commitment exists in the board room, one that is strong enough to unfreeze current behaviours, values and assumptions and enable new ones to take over.

If the organization is not severely threatened, and has both the resources and the time, far-sighted executives can implement change step by step. By consistent use of every opportunity they can move the organization in the right direction and this movement will gather momentum as special emphasis is put on the selection and training of managers.

However, when crisis looms and change is urgently needed, which unfortunately is more usually the case, more energetic action is required. According to Edgar Schein (1988, p. 294) four conditions are necessary if a situation is to be turned around:

1. Top management awareness of the need for change, and readiness to challenge old assumptions and unfreeze the entire organization.
2. The existence of a convincing model.
3. A clear vision of where the organization needs to go.
4. Commitment and power to apply the model to the entire organization and make change permanent.

6.1.1 Awareness: Unfreezing the Organization

External realities, like erosion of market share and profits or heightened competition, may clearly indicate a looming crisis. However, further arguments are usually necessary to convince management of the need to change from steering by cost reduction to heading for quality as its first priority.

As money language seemed to be the only one Western managers appear capable of understanding, in order to create awareness numerous consultants have placed considerable importance on the cost-of-quality argument. What manager can resist the temptation to go for this fantastic gold mine, supposedly representing at least 20 per cent of sales turnover! However, this mythical cost, by definition an aggregate of a host of hidden and often inaccessible costs, remains an overall, theoretical figure, far removed from physical processes.

Other more direct indicators result from an analysis of the competition. Competitive benchmarking, for example, not only compares the performance of different products on the market, their reliability and conformance levels, but also reveals where the differences lie. In 1980 Xerox used benchmarking to explain how Japanese photocopiers could be sold in Europe at a price equal to Xerox's cost price. As CEO David Kearns (1989, p. 19) explained, 'Benchmarking is tearing down the competitor's machine and understanding its costs and reliability aspects ... how they are better than ours .... Now we benchmark everything.'

A competitive benchmark comparing the entire sequence for the production of Japanese and American photocopiers, from design to after-sales, showed up substantial differences in the quality levels of incoming components and materials, and a considerable loss of efficiency due to frequent engineering design changes, etc. Benchmarking used as a diagnostic tool for the entire system showed where improvements could be made to catch up with the competition at a rate of at least 15 per cent productivity gain per annum. And a 15 per cent productivity gain in one place may well mean a 50 per cent reduction of defects and waste in another.

This diagnostic tool can bring management back to basic processes, to how other people got there, to the language of things. By pinning up comparative charts on office and workshop walls, management can convince the entire corporation of the need for change. When the law of the situation is demonstrated in this way, excuses such as 'We aren't doing too badly!', 'That's exactly what the other departments should be doing', and 'That's okay for astronauts walking on the moon!' no longer hold water.

Many other indicators and many other ways of convincing management also exist. In fact, more often than not this new insight coincides with the arrival of a new chief executive who is well acquainted with total quality philosophy, or with a visit to another company where this type of change has been implemented successfully, or with a trip to Japan. Whatever the case, the essential factor is the level of awareness and conviction among the dominant management coalition that will be responsible for proving the need for change to the personnel of the entire organization and that will unfreeze the existing culture and lead the organization to adopt the new model.

6.1.2 Existence of Convincing Model

The key concepts of the new frame of reference have been largely dealt with in the preceding chapters, from the definition of quality and the generalized customer–supplier relationship to the Deming wheel (very similar to the Juran trilogy: quality planning, quality control, quality improvement). They form a basic common language that can facilitate the diffusion of the new cultural model throughout the organization.

What we would like to stress here is that this strategy to regain conformance, this first reform, must be strongly supported by the new assumption that quality, far from being a problem, should be considered as an opportunity, as an economic, social and cultural solution.

- Management for quality is an economic solution. The advantage of measuring the cost of poor quality is mainly conceptual, as it demonstrates clearly that 'Quality is free' (Crosby, 1980). In the long run the total cost of poor quality is reduced if enough resources are invested in prevention, and a better knowledge and control of the system are acquired.

- Management for quality is a social and a cultural solution. Management for quality goes beyond the economic result, and brings in its wake a profound cultural change which simultaneously strengthens the company's potential to adapt by developing human resources and technical know-how.

Let us consider these two aspects in detail.

Management for Quality is an Economic Solution

The cost-of-quality concept can be used to demonstrate that 'quality is free'. In practice, the cost of quality corresponds to expenses which could have been avoided by getting the products or the service right first time. Cost of quality is made up of four costs:

- Prevention costs: project reviews, design reviews, validation, training, maintenance, improvement projects, design of experiments, operating procedures, guidelines, etc.
- Appraisal costs: tests, inspection, audits, surveys, gathering and processing control data, reports, evaluation of suppliers, certification, etc.
- Internal failure costs: scrap, rework, lost time, reruns, unused capacity, engineering changes, etc.
- External failure costs: returns, recalls, complaints, replacements, compensation, field service, repairs under guarantee, product liabilities, etc.

In fact, cost of quality represents an amalgam of every effort aimed at avoiding, filtering out or dealing with non-quality. Just as the water level of a river, that must flow well above the stones and boulders obstructing it, rises to become navigable, so the COQ level rises to cover problems. This level can reach as much as 20 per cent of sales turnover, for companies still at the first stage of awareness.

This potential gold mine often incites the corporation to set up a specific COQ measurement system, since the normal accounting system is unsuitable. In fact, a COQ estimation can only be approximate, for the river must be completely drained if a systematic census of all non-quality costs is to be carried out. The work is enormous and frequently illusory, since in most cases only the symptoms, the foam on the waves, are visible in a rapidly changing system. We should note that the old management habit of concentrating attention on costs and on cost cutting still holds. Nevertheless, the concept is still helpful for our demonstration.

A firm unaware of its non-quality problems is in situation I in Figure 6.1. Following awareness, and first developments led by the quality control department, it will be in situation II where failure costs and appraisal costs balance out. COQ is lower but is it possible to get beyond this trade-off? Wisdom begins when the firm

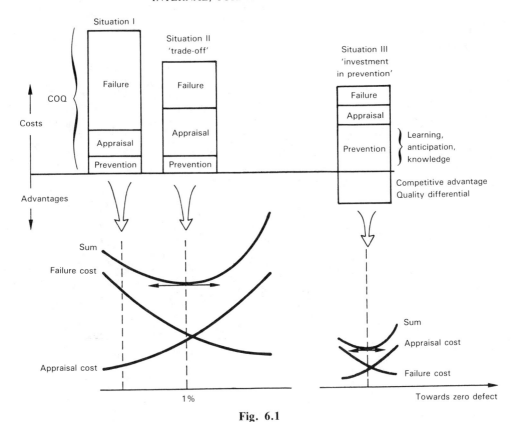

Fig. 6.1

realizes the importance of prevention and makes the trade-off in situation III, and learning and anticipation are substituted for failure and appraisal costs.

The conventional trade-off, appraisal versus failure, can be overcome by the introduction of a third term: prevention or learning. The sooner a defect is screened or prevented, the more savings can be made during latter stages. This can be demonstrated very easily by the following example. Suppose that the cost of preventing the introduction of a defective resistor is arbitrarily 1. If this resistor is soldered onto a circuit board, the cost of detection and repair may be 20 times greater. If the defect is identified at sub-assembly level, the cost may be multiplied by 2. But if the cost is only identified at final inspection, it could be multiplied by 5. Finally, when the item is in the hands of the user and breaks down, the cost may well be 5 times greater again. This means a total multiplicative factor of $20 \times 2 \times 5 \times 5 = 1000$. (See Figure 6.2.)

Thus, by increasing the cost of prevention by 1, it is possible to decrease the detection and failure costs by 1000. This factor may be even higher in services. For example, an undetected writing error in a piece of software can wreak havoc with

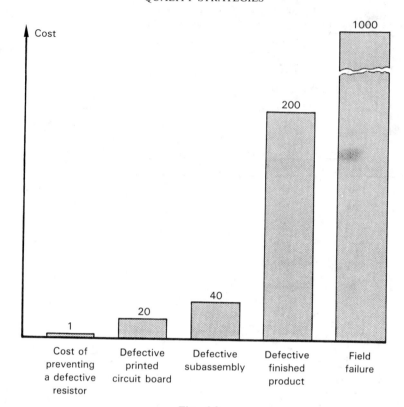

Fig. 6.2

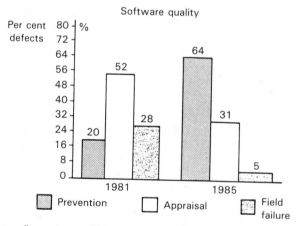

Source: The quality program at IBM, by William Eggleston.
Proceedings of the 4th Annual Operations Management Association Meeting, Nov. 1985.

Fig. 6.3

the client. It is sometimes so difficult to trace the error that the entire piece of software has to be rewritten.

The substantial economies IBM obtained between 1981 and 1985, when they strengthened prevention to improve software quality, can be seen in Figure 6.3. We can imagine the argument that can be developed to justify the large investments necessary for learning and anticipation, when moving from situation II to situation III in Figure 6.1: 'By multiplying prevention costs by a factor of 3, you could divide the cost of quality of your firm by 2, while adding a quality differential.'

This principle of prevention is quite broad, and covers most of the actions we have recommended on the process and on the system. Making every employee responsible for the control of his or her own quality means anticipating downstream inspection. Investing in process capability, in know-how and in improvements means preventing problems. Restoring good customer–supplier relationships means anticipating misunderstanding. Simplifying and returning to the natural flow logic of the process means making problems and waste more visible, etc.

Management for Quality is a Social and Cultural Solution

Development of Responsibility and Autonomy

When information and initiative are decentralized, decisions are taken at source and problems are settled directly between internal customers and suppliers. When employees are more directly responsible for their work, they will develop their potential and use their intelligence to a greater extent. The chain of command is shortened. The autocratic boss who has to be flattered, who gets irritable or is known to impose inappropriate orders and instructions, becomes a thing of the past. The manager becomes more of an expert, a coach, a trainer. He helps to establish suitable standards, makes experimentation and improvement possible, and restores lateral communications.

Staff specialists, considered as suppliers to line personnel, have to give up some of their prerogatives and return to their natural role: that of facilitating the work of front-line operators.

This capacity to act from a sense of ownership is a strong source of motivation. True motivation originates from a natural desire to do well and improve; it is not induced by exhortation and fear. In the carrot and stick approach, the holders of the stick or carrot are the ones that are motivated, the others are simply set in motion.

Development of Co-operation

By breaking down the barriers between departments, by re-establishing interdepartmental, interprocess customer–supplier relations and by multiplying interdisciplinary groups, management for quality reduces lateral tensions and reinforces the internal solidarity and cohesion of the corporate system. While the decentralization of initiative and responsibility leads to greater differentiation and adaptation in the field, co-operation focuses all efforts on a common objective: customer satisfaction and error-free work. This integration of effort characterizes one of the fundamental properties of a system: all the parts work together towards a common goal.

This double movement of decentralization and integration leads to motivation, and an improvement in social indicators such as absenteeism, staff turnover and even occupational accidents.

Management for Quality Introduces a Technical and Professional Culture
According to Edward Hall (1959), culture exists on three levels and along three classes of behaviour: formal, informal and technical.

> The sport of skiing offers an excellent example of the formal, informal, and technical modes. Some years ago in the town of Grand Lake, Colorado, on the snowy western slope of the Rockies, there was a tradition that every-one had to use skis to get around in the wintertime . . . . Small children learned to ski soon after they could walk . . . . Skiing was taken for granted as a part of the daily life of the town; it was . . . a *formal* tradition . . . . At the same time, there were a few hardy souls in Denver and other nearby towns who used to take to skis for pleasure, as a part-time activity. . . . They were not highly conscious of how they skied, what technique they used, or how the skill could be taught. They would say 'Watch me', or 'Do it like this'. . . . Their conception of skiing was *informal*, a view which is no better expressed than in the phrase, 'You'll get the hang of it'.
>
> At the same time . . . thousands of feet of film were being taken in the Alps of wonderfully skilled skiers rushing down slopes, turning, climbing, and coming to a stop. These films were analyzed, and the whole process was broken down into its components or isolates, as they can be called. In addition to the components, broader patterns were also analyzed. After a while it was decided that skiing was not an art which had to be restricted to the gifted. Anyone with patience and a modicum of control could be taught to ski, since the components had been so well identified that they could be talked about and described *technically*. . . . Technical learning . . . is usually transmitted in explicit terms from the teacher to the student . . . and depends . . . more on the intelligence with which the material is analyzed and presented.

It is far easier to introduce changes in the technical culture than in the formal or informal. Technical changes are specific, visible, measurable and easier to analyze and communicate before they solidify into a new formal system with rules, standards and procedures.

Management for quality leads a corporation from informal ways of doing things (behaviour modes learned on the job reinforced by stable formal rules) to a technical, scientific, methodical, statistical culture, far more explicit and open to mastery and progress.

Amateurism, tinkering or problem fixing are no longer sufficient, even if they demonstrate smartness. Every employee becomes a professional in his job, and learns other skills in order to enlarge and enrich his or her working life; informal practice is made visible and measurable. In the new culture, employees analyze every aspect of their work, from the management of their time to their skills levels. They spell out in greater detail the standards and operating procedures of the processes for which they are responsible in order to control them better. They improve them, using statistical techniques, systematic prevention or problem-solving methods. They experiment 'scientifically' by submitting their theories to the judgement of the facts. Like professional athletes, they try to improve their previous record under the guidance of a coach and with the help of a supporting team (doctor, experts...). By broadening their skills, they become more versatile.

It is no longer necessary to restrict activities and classify employees into 80 different categories. Three or four are now sufficient. Decentralization and a shorter chain of command go hand in hand with greater professionalism. Every employee now has access to the technical culture which originates more from their 'scientific' or vocational training, than from their national or local culture. This culture travels well and is easier to transmit than formal or informal culture.

6.1.3 A Clear Vision of Where the Organization Needs to Go

The management for quality presented so far is focused on conformance, error-free work and waste elimination. Because the concepts are simple and easy to explain, a common language, applicable to most situations, spreads throughout the organization. The method has certain similarities with financial management control, but instead of concentrating on financial and cost deviations it searches out pockets of non-quality and non-added value due to physical malfunctions in the processes and in the system.

To be convincing, management for quality must be integrated in the management system and the corporate strategy. Ambitious goals will demonstrate that top management is determined to carry out the quality revolution successfully. By launching a challenge which strikes the imagination, the management team can start to unfreeze the organization, and mobilize it in a new direction. The choice of goals and the ease and visibility of measurements are therefore essential. Giving clear directions does not mean managing by objectives. Too many companies are under-led, but overmanaged. Let us take a few examples of some possible objectives:

- Divide cost of quality by 2 in less than five years.
- Improve reliability by a factor of 10 (Hewlett Packard in 1980).
- Reduce final defect rate on integrated circuits from 5000 ppm to 100 ppm in five years (Texas Instruments HIJI plant in Japan in 1980).
- Launch the 552 campaign this year (50 per cent inventory reduction, 50 per cent defect reduction, 20 per cent productivity gain), and the 663 campaign next year (Mazda, the Japanese auto manufacturer).

These directions can be structured along three main lines:

Reference to Final Customer
- Level of complaints and claims. Complaints are a lagging indicator which only represent the tip of the iceberg. For every customer who complains, there are many more dissatisfied customers who remain silent but switch to the competition.
- Customer satisfaction level and loyalty monitored by systematic surveys.
- After-sales defect rate or reliability. Warranty and service reports.

Reference to the Competition
- Company ranking relative to the competition.
- Competitive benchmarking.

Specific Physical Indicators Identified by Internal Audits and In-house Surveys
Problems and malfunctions are not uniformly distributed throughout the manufacturing and delivery cycle, and some departments may have a larger share than others. If, for example, an audit discovers that this is the case in the design department, then clear objectives should be given as to the reduction of, say, engineering changes or shorter lead times for new product introduction.

Cost of Quality Again

In the West, the cost of quality has assumed far greater importance than in Japan. One reason for this is the need to find a financial argument to convince those 'bottom line' managers who are overly concerned with short-term results. Japanese managers, by contrast, are already convinced that quality is beneficial in the long run and have lower short-term pressure.

However attractive the concept may appear, COQ has serious drawbacks if used as a measuring tool.

- The poor quality is naturally concealed below the surface of the process flow, or by the fog surrounding the system, so it would be quite a feat to make a thorough count of all the hidden non-qualities.
- The COQ tends to discount qualitative aspects and long-term vision. Once again, any financial measurement of the result tends to discount the physical factors which are more difficult to quantify: inventory reduction, better use of capacity, shorter lead times, or improvement opportunities which only appear in the field. Because they are not intimately familiar with the production processes for which they are responsible, some managers tend to rely on short-term financial criteria and COQ.
- It is difficult to estimate the contribution of each department. What is the contribution of poor design or long process set-up to the total COQ. While some costs may be counted several times over, others may be forgotten.

- COQ is unsuitable for comparative purposes. A department with frequent new product launches will have a much higher COQ than a department producing the same component over several years. COQ is not the most critical factor to be considered when introducing new products. Time is a far more sensitive and decisive indicator.

Planning Directions

The deployment policy of projects and team activities should, of course, be based on audits and field analysis of the situation. These should form part of the overall corporate strategy and be gradually institutionalized. Overall quality objectives and requirements, broken down into sub-objectives at department or process level, can provide a reference framework for initiative proposals and actions coming from the field. There should be a dual movement, top down and bottom up.

Proposals and projects should be negotiated and accepted provided they are in line with targets after consolidation. Clearly the cycle must be repeated frequently, in order to reach the right consistency between the deployment plan and reality in the field. If targets are not achieved, objectives should be revised or discrepancies analyzed, and new projects proposed. The policy deployment exercise is important in that learning is acquired during the planning process. It is a good vehicle for reminding line personnel of the things top management considers to be important and worthy of their attention. Table 6.1 is an example of how projects can be consolidated into an annual plan.

Table 6.1

Progress objectives Department X	Goal	Estimated resources	Timing	Measurable target indicator	Project leader
Proposal 1 Solve problem A					
Proposal 2 Solve problem B					
Proposal 3 Reduce administrative cost for operation C					
Proposal 4 Improve yield of process D					
Proposal 5 Reduce cycletime of process flow E					
Sum of all proposals					
Global objective					

• 119 •

6.1.4 Commitment and Power to Apply the Model

The quality cultural reform cannot be set in motion unless the old management ways are unfrozen. Key executives must lead and steer change with unflagging determination, and long-term visible commitment. How, then, can they convince the entire staff of the necessity for change, and of their determination to mobilize everyone in the organization?

The answer is by setting an example and being a role model, by dramatizing the situation and offering new values, by reassuring the risk takers, by changing what is at stake, by encouraging learning and co-operation and by choosing and rewarding those who share this new vision. In all these ways, management can pave the way for the new practices that will create the new culture.

Convincing

Public statements, quality charters, exhortations, poster campaigns and slogans are all useful provided they are part of an overall project. On their own, however, they are no more than ritual incantations. The 'Hawthorn' effect only elicits goodwill and unfreezes behaviour for a short time. (This is a motivation effect caused by special attention from management. Its name comes from Mayo experiments in 1934 at the Hawthorn plant of Western Electric. By observing the effect of working conditions on the productivity of operators assembling relays he noted that productivity continued to improve even if working conditions grew worse. This was due simply to the attention devoted to the subject by management and research team.)

An organization cannot be changed by proclamation. A good axiom says that 'they watch your feet not your lips'! Key executives can convince the rest of the organization by their visible behaviour, by being role models, by being consistent and showing that their actions match their words. This consistency of behaviour and constancy of purpose are very important for communicating new values, for managers are constantly observed informally. Quality importance and priority should be stressed in everyday business operations, and appear as a regular agenda item at staff planning meetings.

Some external indicators such as COQ, profit and market share decline or competitive benchmarking can be used to dramatize the situation, and help unfreeze the organization.

Promoting and Recruiting

The replacement of people in critical positions, performance appraisal, promotion and status are all clear signs of what an organization values. According to Edgar

Schein (1988, pp. 235, 236), 'Basic assumptions are reinforced through criteria of who does not get promoted, who is retired early, and who is, in effect excommunicated', and 'Culture perpetuates itself through the recruitment of people.' At Xerox, for example, the promotion of senior executives is linked to their level of quality involvement and initiative. As chairman David Kearns (1989, p. 19) pointed out,

> There are three categories which are easy to understand. The first level is that when talking about quality, your use of the tools and your understanding of it, make you a role model. You are an example. Your people understand it. The second level is where I can say you are competent, but not yet a role model. In other words you understand it. The third level is that you need work. Those are three terms in this company that people are beginning to understand. When senior people get their review, if it says 'need work', that affects their bonus, their pay and their eligibility for promotion, which is the thing that bothered them most.

Reassuring

Change can only proceed through practice and experiment with new modes of behaviour. To enable people to unfreeze the system and question their own practices, a positive climate has to be created where everyone is entitled to experiment, even if it leads to errors at the start. Zero defects do not mean the outright rejection of any possibility of mistakes being made, for that would result in a fear of trying new ways. What it does mean is learning from errors or past ways.

Non-added values and hidden problems will only become visible once blame and fear have been eliminated. A formal policy statement promising security of employment should be considered, as a step in this direction.

To encourage people further to start out on the road to change, long-term commitment should be clearly demonstrated and it should be clear that the dominant management coalition will be in charge throughout the long haul. The 'flavour of the month' syndrome is avoided by sending clear signals. Thus, the executive in charge of the change process should not be perceived as being in a dead-end job. Managers should remain in the same position long enough to see their project right through to its conclusion. (A manager who knows he will not be staying in his job more than two years is not going to work harder for his successor than for himself).

Reorganizing the System and Providing Resources

Management is responsible for reorganizing the system, reducing superstructures, turning the pyramid upside down (staff as support to line), empowering people down the line and restoring certain forms of co-operation (partnership with external suppliers, integration of new product development efforts, multiplication of cross-functional quality projects, etc.).

All this means deciding how to allocate time and resources, clear indicators of what management pays attention to. As David Kearns added, in the interview cited above, 'During some expense crunch times, keeping the number of quality people we have, has been a good signal as well, especially when all the other resources and staffs have been reduced. People watch resource allocation very, very carefully.'

Knowing and Monitoring the Change Process

Top managers should be part of the steering committee monitoring the change process, and should have a say in the selection of essential projects and the choice of team members. To set an example, they may even participate in vital projects. They should also monitor key indicators, and the results of regular audits and surveys.

Management should also carefully monitor the progress of the change process itself: the number of active quality improvement teams or quality circles, value analysis workshops, the number of certified suppliers, personnel satisfaction index, etc. Management should also spend a lot of time communicating, explaining, training, rewarding and celebrating, as we will see in the next section. Let us cite David Kearns once more. In reply to an ingenuous friend who asked him, 'David, why did you go through all this stuff? It really seems process-bound and complicated. Why didn't you just stand up and tell people what you wanted them to do?' David Kearns answered: 'I tried that. It didn't work ... You get down to the nitty-gritty, which is not very exciting. But the two keys are understanding the depth and turning people on!'

6.2   KEY ELEMENTS OF THE CHANGE PROCESS

Once top management is clearly and visibly committed, spreading the change process will be facilitated by the following:

1.   A steering committee to co-ordinate actions and plan change.
2.   Communication and internal marketing.
3.   Methods and education.
4.   Recognition of merits and celebration of results.

6.2.1   A Steering Committee to Co-ordinate Actions and Plan Change

Total quality should sweep through the business vertically and laterally with a systemic logic. Improvement in one sector may influence or complicate the task of another. All improvements should be integrated along common directions.

But who should be responsible for continuous improvement and ambitious quality targets? Managers, of course, as if they do not already have enough to do! The new motto is 'Do it right the first time, and even better the second time.' But to change the behaviour of every manager in the organization is no easy task. Moreover, because opportunities for improvement and interaction are numerous, it is essential to set up a steering body to manage the change process until new behaviour modes are fully integrated.

This committee, often called the quality steering committee or quality council or TQC promotion centre, should be involved in planning, project selection, choice of team managers and members for major projects and monitoring progress. Monitoring progress means not only measuring internal and external results (defect rates, field failures, etc.) but evaluating the change itself (number of active projects, of implemented projects, training efforts, communication efforts, personnel motivation, etc.).

The steering committee may be assisted by a 'quality bureau' or a 'quality team central' to do more administrative and consultancy tasks (computer program tracking of all projects with their status, for example). This bureau may be headed by a spokesperson, 'the great communicator' to champion the change process. Given its strategic role, the steering committee should be composed of the most influential executives in each sector (In large firms there may be committees at different levels: corporate, division, department etc.), fully determined to get things going. It would be an error, however, to appoint as leader of the committee somebody too closely associated with the quality assurance department. It is essential to avoid any confusion between a cultural change process and the quality assurance function.

To conduct the change, to regulate its speed and spread, the steering committee must define specific policies such as:

- Should participation in quality improvement teams be voluntary or mandatory? The advantage of mandatory participation is that it can force through change by squeezing middle managers between top down pressure and bottom up initiatives. A more participative approach may encourage experimentation and learning, but may lack sufficient strength.
- How long should a manager or a supervisor stay in the same job? Long enough to become well acquainted with the job, learn it and improve himself by seeing the fruits of his efforts, but not so long that boredom and routine set in.
- Who or what should guide the improvement team? The hierarchical boss, a facilitator trained in problem-solving methods and group dynamics, or the 'mission' assigned to the group?
- How are the results of improvement teams to be assessed? Should they be allowed to implement their solutions immediately?

6.2.2 Communication and Internal Marketing

Change has to be explained, 'sold' or encouraged, while uncertainty and anxiety have to be reduced. All the usual media tools are valid: newsletters, lectures, visits, the recounting of successful experiments, publications, advertisements, posters, a corner in the workshop where activities can be publicized, etc. New slogans, stories, myths and parables can illustrate history and spread the new concepts and new values. These will gradually be formalized and crystallized in the organization. What are the new beliefs of our cultural reform?

Former convictions	*New convictions*
1. The primary mission of production is cost reduction.	1. The primary mission of production is quality.
2. Improving quality is expensive.	2. Costs cannot be reduced without affecting quality. But quality can be improved without increasing cost, and may even lead to cost reduction.
3. Quality is a matter for specialists. Quality is the manufacturing department's job. Good workers make good quality.	3. Quality is the responsibility of everyone in the organization.
4. Top management deals with strategy, marketing and finance.	4. Top management must be involved in operational processes and not merely in results.
5. The benefits of any action can be measured financially at the outset and rapidly added to the bottom line.	5. Total quality is difficult to evaluate but pays off economically and socially in the long term.
6. It is better to await the next reorganization before improving things.	6. A host of small improvements over the entire system has a determining cumulative effect.
7. A manager's priority should be the maximization of the results of his department.	7. Total quality is systemic: a local improvement does not necessarily improve the results of the entire system.
8. You cannot trust suppliers.	8. Certain suppliers can become partners.
9. Marketing and engineering define the product. Production merely has to carry out orders.	9. Production is the customer of the engineering design department and should be listened to carefully.
10. Operators are paid to do, not to think.	10. Human capital is the primary resource of any organization.

11. It is forbidden to get it wrong, failure is evil.	11. You can learn from your mistakes. You should thank anyone who points out an error.
12. There is no point in repairing something that does not break 'If it ain't broke, don't fix it.'	12. Prevention is curing.
13. What can you do for me?	13. What can I do for you?
14. You cannot change people's attitudes.	14. By using professionals you can aim at excellence.
15. Mistakes and errors are problems and deserve blame.	15. Problems are welcome opportunities for improvement.

6.2.3 Methods and Education

In a more technical and professional culture, careful staff recruitment, promotion and education become vital dimensions. K. Ishikawa maintains that quality begins and ends with education. The investment required to develop know-how and make personnel multiskilled can be substantial, but by it, human capital becomes the primary resource of the corporation.

The diagnosis and annual plan of action developed by a steering committee should analyze current skills and training needs in the following areas:

Development of personal effectiveness:
● time management
● group dynamics
● leadership

Total quality concepts and quality assurance

Tools and methods: statistics, how to collect and use data, quality control, design of experiments, problem solving, value engineering, reliability, maintainability, FMEA, etc.

Development of craftsmanship and know-how: for management to be truly committed to the process, it is essential that training be carried out from top to bottom, with managers involved as much as possible. Managers should increasingly act as consultants, experts and educators.

Finally, we should note that change only becomes operational if it is the result of regular practice. It is therefore necessary to multiply opportunities for practice and experiment through action training. The concepts are experimented on, even while they are being taught.

6.2.4 Recognition of Merits and Celebration of Results

There are many ways of recognizing and rewarding those who have contributed to

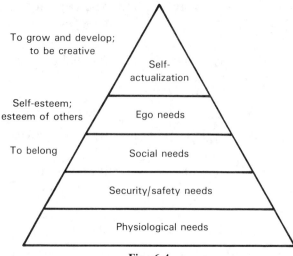

Fig. 6.4

the success of the change project. They can be classified according to the Maslow motivation pyramid. (See Figure 6.4.) It should be noted that recognition should not only concern the result and the money saved but also the process, the effort, the good work, the learning and the new skills, etc. Competition between groups should be encouraged.

Results-linked bonuses (more a reward than a motivator) may correspond to the bottom and third levels of the Maslow pyramid, as they are accompanied by promotion and social recognition. The possible signs of social recognition are manifold, and management needs to be extremely imaginative: gifts, medals, ribbons, handshakes, listening to presentations, trips, citations, photographs, a free lunch with key executives, planting a tree with your name on it, your weight in cans of beer, etc.

At the highest level, what counts is free time, personal development (education, etc.) or promotion and power. Recognition of merit goes hand in hand with celebration, the party where everybody gathers to celebrate accomplishments.

6.3 CONCLUSION

The journey towards conformity sets out defensively, in an attempt to make up for complacency and loss of professionalism. However, as its internal capacities are gradually strengthened, the corporation is better able to establish competitive advantage. The result is better conformance, better durability, greater reliability until, with better service and specific advantages, quality finally takes the offensive. We shall examine this new aspect in the next chapter.

CHAPTER 7

•

QUALITY AS A STRATEGIC
SOLUTION: THE SECOND REFORM –
AN OFFENSIVE STRATEGY

The three previous chapters dealt with the first phase of the quality reformation. This portrayed quality as an economic and social solution rather than a problem, one able to deliver a promised offer through a systematic and disciplined internal mobilization which reduced error and waste, while bringing all the benefits of increased co-operation.

However, although it is true that a reduction in the number of defects and perceived minuses can provide some advantage compared with an even worse competitor, that advantage still remains a passive one. Eliminating the minuses will give the client fewer grounds for complaint, but not more reason to buy. So although quality of conformity is necessary it is not by itself sufficient, as it does not provide the pluses which make all the difference.

The next phase of the quality reformation, the second reform, can rectify this omission by helping the organization to take that extra step, and so move from a position of quality by default to one of quality by excess. Quality is thereby transformed from a passive property into a strategic weapon, one that can be wielded in the market place to devastating effect.

This second cultural reform is total inasmuch as everyone in the organization has access to the strategy and understands his or her role within it. This is not just to give the 'normal' satisfaction the client is entitled to expect, but to build the competitive advantage which will make the difference and delight the customer. Thus, the customer is reintegrated into the overall production and delivery process, and the employees become not just responsible to their line managers, but are brought face to face with the authority of the client and the market.

Against this backcloth, constant adjustments will be required to counter the moves made by competitors. As they fill the gaps and create new advantages, the corporation must then find ways of surpassing them. In this way, a quality dynamic is set in motion.

By this, total quality permeates every process, is gradually deployed throughout the corporate system and becomes associated with other missions, notably delivery, cost and flexibility. Once again the driving force must be the management team; dedicated to leading the change and organizing new forms of co-operation.

This chapter is divided into three main parts:

1. Processes revitalized by quality.
2. Deploying quality throughout the system.
3. External turnaround strategy.

7.1 PROCESSES REVITALIZED BY QUALITY

7.1.1 Differentiation Through Reduced Dispersion

A process is a series of operations leading to a final result in the form of a component, a finished product or a service. Naturally, the final result will vary from one product to another, but once the process is under control it will be statistically distributed according to a 'normal' law. This natural dispersion reflects the addition of all sorts of minor variations occasioned by random common causes. The process is considered capable if the tolerances defined by the design department amply cover this normal dispersion. (See Figure 7.1.)

As long as production remains within the design tolerance limits it is considered to be formally right, and all products whose characteristics are within the tolerance limits are considered equally right, however close they may be to those limits. Outside these limits, the product is considered defective and must be repaired at a cost (cost A in Figure 7.1). Similarly, all products falling outside the tolerance limits, whatever their distance from them, are considered equally defective. The logic here is binary: the product is either good or defective. The cost step function is A outside the tolerance limits, and zero within them. This applies to all the major characteristics of the product or the service.

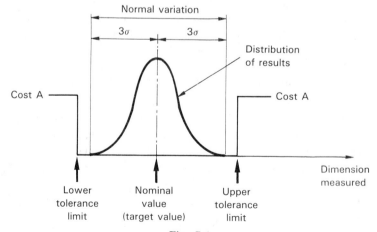

Fig. 7.1

Customers, however, do not have the same perception as the engineering department. They really do see a difference between a product having characteristics close to the nominal value (the optimum value calculated by an engineer and assumed to give the best result) and a product with characteristics close to the reject limit. To them, all products within tolerance limits are not of equal quality. Tolerance was invented by engineers, but the customer contracts for the nominal product every time, as observed by Mr Pierre Jocou, Director of Quality with Renault, 'Renault does not sell 8000 cars a day, but one car 8000 times over.'

Similarly, airline passengers want the plane to leave within one minute of the scheduled time, whereas airport engineers consider the plane is still on time within a 15-minute delay. Many other examples can be given: a television set, properly adjusted to the nominal values, gives a sharper image; a well-adjusted car door closes with the satisfying noise the customer recognizes in a luxury car. The engine runs like clockwork, almost noiselessly, etc.

To take account of this phenomenon Taguchi suggested replacing the cost step function by a parabolic loss function around the nominal value. This is shown in Figure 7.2. The loss due to non-quality increases as the square of the deviation, as soon as the result deviates from the nominal value. If the loss is constant, with cost A outside the limits and cost zero inside, conformity to specifications is a formal measurement, based on current process capabilities. This measurement remains internally orientated, and does not take into account the interests of the customers or society at large. A tolerance, as the very name indicates, is an allowance granted by engineers because of their inability to do otherwise. However, an organization should never lose sight of the nominal value, but constantly seek to reduce the degree of variation in order to remain as close to it as possible.

Since the final dispersion is the sum of every local dispersion at the various stages

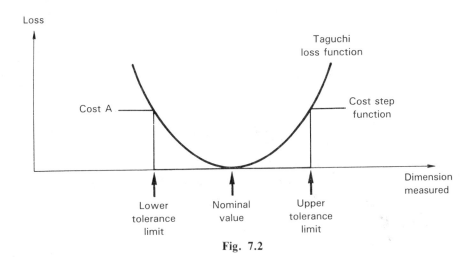

Fig. 7.2

of the production process, everyone should constantly strive to reduce the variation of his or her results at their own level. This new challenge will lead the organization deeper and deeper into the new professional and disciplined practice of total quality.

Dispersion is the enemy which must be fought, project by project. In the long run, the difference will become plainly visible, making the product's superiority over that of a competitor radical. If this drive for reduced dispersion is missing, everyone will take full advantage of the given allowance to work within the tolerance limits, and the final product characteristics will spread out over the entire tolerance window. As everyone knows, what is not forbidden is allowed. The final spread will absorb all successive dispersions and may eventually exceed acceptable limits. Quality inspection will then be needed in order to eliminate and correct the distribution 'tails' outside the tolerance limits. (See Figure 7.3.)

From the customer's viewpoint, differences do exist. The television set works, but the colours are not as bright, the picture not as sharply-defined as on the set produced in a competitor's factory, where dimensions are kept closer to nominal values. Or perhaps the car engine makes strange noises; the door on the new car does not close at first try. Yet any complaint will be denied. The customer will be shown that they are mistaken, as the product in question conforms perfectly with design specifications. Besides, improvements would cost too much, better to save them for the next model.

On the other hand, the producer who strives to reduce dispersion at every step, in line with Taguchi's philosophy, will find the final distributions better concentrated around the nominal values; the engine will run better, the colours will be brighter and so on.

As an illustration, let us take the manufacture of ball-bearings where the

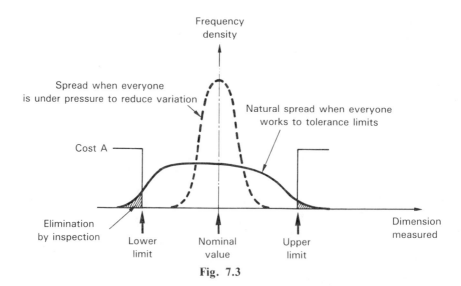

Fig. 7.3

dispersion is well inside the accepted variations for key dimensions. The client may have no immediate need of this superiority, but is still being given an opportunity he may later take advantage of in his own production process. Progress does not just mean reducing defects or minuses, it also means doing better what you are already doing well. Mr Imai quotes an actual case of a Japanese firm whose industrial engineers worked on this very problem, and finally succeeded in reducing the dispersion of ball-bearing diameters through more frequent tool changes. (See Figure 7.4.) This firm then developed a rapid change of tool method which resulted in much tighter control limits.

If the objective of continuous reduction of dispersion is clearly signalled, everyone can concentrate his energy, imagination and professionalism on this target.

7.1.2 Differentiation by Making the Process More Robust

Providing the customer with something as close as possible to the nominal offer by reducing internal dispersion from one product to the next is one way of adding value. However, there are other sources of dispersion that could be investigated in order to differentiate the product further, and make it more reliable and less sensitive to environmental influences.

Design engineers should not, therefore, call a halt on reaching the first satisfactory formula or acceptable production process but continue to experiment with the objective of defining the formula and process parameters that can eliminate or as far as possible reduce, harmful influences associated with external variations in the environment (temperature or raw material variations) or internal deterioration during usage (wear, breakdown).

Parameter Design

The process set up to manufacture a product or deliver a service is conditioned by a certain number of parameters, generally grouped into five categories: raw

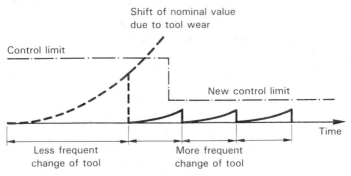

Fig. 7.4

materials; machines; formula and methods of production; labour force; and environment. In the simplest case of quantitative variables, each parameter is characterized by a nominal value and an allowed variation. When all the parameters remain within the prescribed limits, the process is under control and the result is normally distributed. (See Figure 7.5.)

But is it possible to go further and search for a better formula? In other words, by combining the nominal values of the parameters differently, is it possible to obtain a robust nominal result with a reduced dispersion, or one that is less influenced by non-controllable disturbances?

The answer is, of course, that it is possible. The method is to test the effect of variations of the parameters around their set nominal values on the final result systematically, with the objective of diminishing the harmful influence of non-controllable causes.

The following example, quoted by Taguchi and Wu (1985, pp. 50–3), demonstrates the principle of parameter design. In the manufacture of ceramic tiles, an essential requirement is regularity of dimension. An analysis of this process demonstrated that the main factors influencing tile dimensions were as shown in Figure 7.6. A very simple experimental plan proposed eight experiments to test the seven factors (A, B, C, D, E, F, G) at two levels: the current formula and the new formula. (See Tables 7.1 and 7.2. Here, A1 is referred to as level 1 for factor A and A2 as level 2 for the same factor A, etc.)

As can be seen from Table 7.2, the average number of defective tiles for the factor A is as follows:

Parameter design

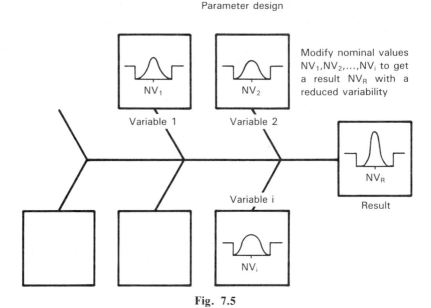

Fig. 7.5

for level 1 of A (A1 = 5 per cent): $\dfrac{16 + 17 + 12 + 6}{4} = 12.75$

for level 2 of A (A2 = 1 per cent): $\dfrac{6 + 68 + 42 + 26}{4} = 35.50$

Statistical calculations show that the difference between the two A levels is significant, the influence of the other factors being cancelled out by the structure of the 'orthogonal' experimental plan (the same amount of levels 1 and 2 for factors B, C, D, E, F, G, in the first four experiments and in the last four).

From the systematic statistical study (that will not be developed here) it was concluded that by increasing the proportion of lime, from 1 to 5 per cent, the dispersion of tile dimensions (and thus the number of defectives) could be significantly reduced and made far less dependent on oven temperature, the most

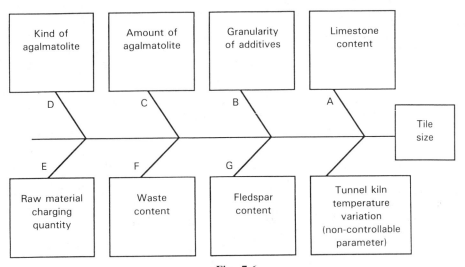

Fig. 7.6

Table 7.1

	Current formula	New formula
Factor A: Limestone content	A2 = 1%	A1 = 5%
Factor B: Fineness of additive	B1 = coarser	B2 = finer
Factor C: Content of agalmatolite	C2 = 53%	C1 = 43%
Factor D: Kind of agalmatolite	D1 = existing combination	D2 = new combination (lower cost)
Factor E: Raw material charging quantity	E2 = 1200 kg	E1 = 1300 kg
Factor F: Content of waste return	F2 = 4%	F1 = 0
Factor G: Content of feldspar	G2 = 5%	G1 = 0

Table 7.2

	Level of factor							Result
Experiment	A	B	C	D	E	F	G	Number of defectives in 100 tiles
1	1	1	1	1	1	1	1	16
2	1	1	1	2	2	2	2	17
3	1	2	2	1	1	2	2	12
4	1	2	2	2	2	1	1	6
5	2	1	2	1	2	1	2	6
6	2	1	2	2	1	2	1	68
7	2	2	1	1	2	2	1	42
8	2	2	1	2	1	1	2	26
								193 out of 800 or 24.13 on average

influential uncontrollable variable affecting size variation. This example shows how, by modifying the formula or operating conditions, it is possible to make a process far less sensitive to the uncontrolled variations of an internal or external parameter.

Allowance Design

But is it possible to reduce dispersion of the results even further? After optimizing the formula or the operating conditions to improve process capability and robustness, efforts may be concentrated on minimizing the allowance given to the variation of some parameters. As some parameters and operating conditions have a major influence on the final result, their range of variation must be controlled and reduced. Another series of experiments can help reduce the causes of final dispersion. (See Figure 7.7.)

Returning to the example of the manufacture of ceramic tiles, if, due to the purity of the lime supplied or the mechanical feeding and mixing process adopted or for any other reason, the proportion of lime added has a range of variation of ± 1 per cent, this tolerance may have a substantial influence on the results, i.e. tile size, inasmuch as there is a clearly proven sensitivity to the presence of lime. Let us therefore assume that, under normal operating conditions, the amount of lime normally varies between 4 per cent and 6 per cent for a nominal value of 5 per cent. Should a series of experiments prove that this range of variation is too high it will

ALLOWANCE DESIGN

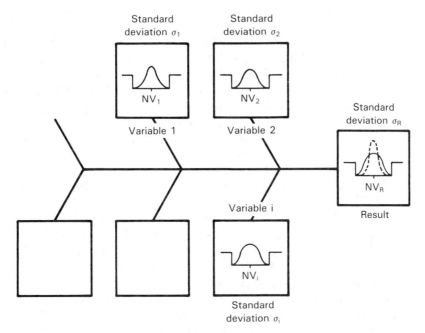

Fig. 7.7

have to be reduced, which ultimately means increasing the capability of the lime distribution process.

Conversely, the strict imposition of tolerances on some other factors may have much less influence on the dispersion of results. As in the previous case, experiments can reveal which influential parameters need to be monitored, and how closely. Clearly, the result of all this hard work will be to go beyond the strict conformity limits defined by engineers, and to market stronger and more reliable products.

7.1.3 Broadening of Total Quality Concept to Cover All Missions

There is no reason to stop there and limit the total quality thrust to improved conformity and reliability, or more robust processes. The same method could also be applied to reliability of delivery and lead time reduction or to flexibility of response. In other words, it can cover the four basic missions of any process: quality, delivery, flexibility and cost. On a production line, for example, these four basic missions are inextricably linked.

Ideally, a repetitive process should flow regularly and smoothly, with the least possible inventory between stations. Defect and breakdown reduction go hand in hand with cycle time reduction. In order to provide variety of output where the flow remains constant (even where 400 cars are produced regularly every day, they could all be different), the process should be made flexible (short set-up times and instant tool changes).

Total quality is thus inextricably linked with efforts to reduce inventory by just-in-time methods of the MRP (material resource planning) type when flows are irregular, or of the Kanban type when flows are regular. Rapid set-ups allow both batch size reduction (therefore smaller inventory) and a more flexible process. However, inventory reduction and tighter flows imply machines which no longer break down, and therefore investments have to be made in preventive maintenance, as illustrated in TPM (total productive maintenance) type methods.

$$TQM \leftrightarrow JIT \leftrightarrow TPM$$
Total Quality management $\leftrightarrow$ Just In Time $\leftrightarrow$ Total Productive Maintenance

All this fits neatly together. Inventory reduction improves quality and vice versa. If, instead of a wall of 10 000 items between one workshop and the next, there are only two containers of fifty items, feedback information when a component is defective is immediate and the number of parts lost is minimal, not to mention that there is substantial reduction in space and cycle time.

And what about the cost of all this? Cost reduction is a natural consequence of process improvement. Improving a process means working on its three main physical dimensions; quality, delivery and flexibility under the cost constraint.

The technical and professional determination to upgrade process performance as far as possible naturally leads to operators and supervisors taking over not only a major portion of manufacturing quality responsibility, but also some responsibility for scheduling (Kanban), maintenance (TPM), set-up, simplification, methods and lay-out, updating of operational procedures, training and even hiring. (See Figure 7.8.)

An Illustration: The NUMMI Experiment

In 1983, General Motors and Toyota joined forces to manufacture and sell a small-sized automobile in the United States. Through this NUMMI (New United Motors Manufacturing Incorporated) experiment, General Motors was hoping to learn and integrate Japanese efficiency and effectiveness for small-car production into its Detroit plant. The Japanese, for their part, were undoubtedly looking upon it as a full-scale manufacturing test in the United States. The ten concepts that guided the experiment clearly illustrate everything that has been said so far:

1. Jidoka: the machine serves the man. For example, an operator can stop the line.
2. Kaizen: continuing improvement.

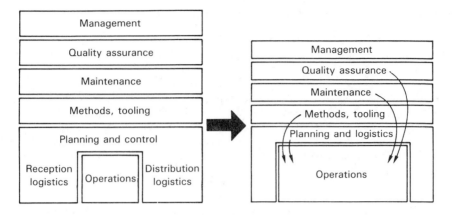

Re-professionalization of operations

Fig. 7.8

3. Elimination of:
   Muda = errors, defects
   Muri = excess
   Mura = irregularities.
4. The five Whys: put the question 'why?' five times running. When solving a problem, seek out the fundamental causes.
5. Good housekeeping:
   Seiri = a clean workplace
   Seiton = a place for everything
   Seiso = clearing
   Seiketsu = regular practice
6. Just-in-time: tighter flows and inventory reduction.
7. Reduction of non-added values (overheads, material handling): be clear as to what the customer needs.
8. Training.
9. Teamwork and share-out of responsibilities.
10. Trust and respect of others: open questioning, avoiding a climate of fear.

7.2 DEPLOYING QUALITY THROUGHOUT THE SYSTEM

The quality imperative should not make us passive, afraid of making mistakes and confined to our shells, to the square defined by the engineers. We should not forget that survival in an open environment, under keen competitive pressure, requires constant adaptation. This factor did not escape the attention of Tom Watson Senior when he was Chairman of IBM. As Peter and Waterman recounted in their book *In Search of Excellence* (1982, p. 159),

> 'I was at a meeting of sales managers with Mr Watson (Senior) one time', says Gordon Smith, recently retired from Memorex. 'The purpose was to assess some customer problems. On the front table there were eight or ten piles of papers, identifying the source of the problems: "manufacturing problems", "engineering problems", and the like. After much discussion, Mr Watson, a big man, walked slowly to the front of the room and, with a flash of his hand, swept the table clean and sent papers flying all over the room. He said, "There aren't any categories of problems here. There's just one problem. Some of us aren't paying enough attention to our customers." He turned crisply on his heel and walked out, leaving twenty fellows wondering whether or not they still had jobs.'

7.2.1 Deploying the Voice of the Customer or In-depth Marketing

While a product or service must correspond to the customer's expectations (some of them latent or unclearly expressed), the fact that the marketing target is global means that it certainly cannot fulfil them all, plus any special requests. Positioning a product or service necessitates a certain degree of standardization to cover a wide enough target, even if later a competitive differentiation must be found.

There is a danger that an excessive 'marketing' view might lead to undue stress being placed on some distinctive feature rather than more solidly based differences. For example, should a car smell of good leather, or should it be highly reliable?

Once the basic concept or formula has been defined, it is combined with the other three elements of the marketing mix: price, promotion and distribution channels or networks in order to position the product or the service *vis-à-vis* competition. The final characteristics of the offer will then endeavour to translate the voice of the customer internally, in the form of quantified specifications. For example, the qualitative feeling of comfort promised by the air-conditioning system of a car is translated into a specific air flow at a certain temperature, so many minutes after the car is started. Needs and expectations are transformed into final characteristics and contract specifications.

The voice of the customer, expressed in terms of technical specifications, is propagated throughout the system, and gradually distorted and reduced at each interface between departments or processes. An analysis of this horizontal deployment and deformation is an important source of improvement.

The deployment of the customer's voice is also described as the quality factoring:

> We take the quality features required of the final system and factor these into quality features in the design, in the code, in the user manuals, in the test specifications, etc. Performance quality features on the design have to be factored further down into individual modules. (Ould, 1990, p. 142)

We should note that transmission of the customer's message is not unidirectional. The choices available to the product creator are limited by the system's capacities and constraints, while conversely the system is a source of proposals and opportunities for a better offer. Every internal customer–supplier relationship should, therefore, operate in both directions to permit dynamic adaptation to the 'voice of the final customer'. (See Figure 7.9.) Clearly, the fewer interfaces there are, the better the message will be transmitted and the better access each employee will have to the customer.

This new reform is vastly more ambitious than the previous one, which had the limited objective of conformity to specifications. The exercise is now broader and more dynamic, for once attuned to the customer, the sources of improvement become inexhaustible. The proposed offer can be enriched as the product evolves with time and matures on the product life-curve and, since competitive advantages do not last long (being rapidly copied by the ever present competition), the customer gradually gets more and more value.

The technical and professional culture described in the previous chapter is well adapted to this unending, methodical and inexorable voyage of improvement.

7.2.2 Contingent Quality Strategies: From Controlled Innovation to Controlled Improvement

The chosen modes of satisfaction, and the competitive advantages employed in the system, will naturally depend on the position of the product or service in its life cycle, whether it is in the introductory, growth or maturity phase. Over these three phases, the client's focus of interest moves from new performances and special characteristics proposed by innovation, to availability and conformity to specification as volume grows, and finally to service or reliability when the offer matures. As the product becomes more standard, the competitive difference will focus on increasingly minor but decisive dimensions. Though price will remain important, it will not always be the determining factor.

During the first stage the corporation defines the formula and positions the new product by trial and error. Innovation puts the design and development department in the front line, and at this so-called fluid stage, the product is mainly characterized by its design and performances.

A quality plan, and well-defined verification, validation, and certification procedures at the various phases of development can help to minimize modifications at

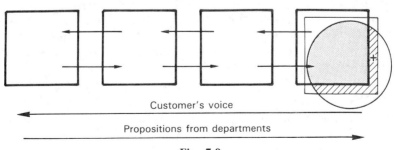

Customer's voice

Propositions from departments

Fig. 7.9

later stages. In fact, this fluid stage requires considerable organizational flexibility to allow the final product characteristics to be adjusted to the fluctuating demands of the market. If knowledge of the manufacturing processes is insufficient, the final inspection will have to be temporarily reinforced, as the corporation will be judged primarily on its ability to control creation and design, to market a product better than the one it is replacing or that is already on the market, or to launch a new product in the shortest time possible.

During the second stage, the corporation establishes its new product by developing the necessary production capacity to gain solid market share before the final shake out. To control increasing volumes fully while maintaining irreproachable conformity to specifications, the corporation must invest massively in industrial engineering.

The main risk at this stage is that under pressure of demand and of production programmes, quality may be relegated to a back seat. Quality must remain the top priority, and the only way to ensure that is through investment in industrial engineering, in industrial learning and in training. Management for quality requires a capable system, capable processes and capable human resources, all deployed to maintain the promised and perceived satisfaction even in the face of a rapid volume build up.

During the third stage, the product becomes standardized and market share is consolidated. Differentiation is based on cost reduction and improvement. There are no longer major innovations to be made in either product or process, but rather incremental improvements in performance, attractiveness, reliability, service and assistance, lead time or flexibility. The emphasis on cost reduction at this stage should not lead to management by cost cutting, as this carries the risk of reducing quality and flexibility of differentiation. The quality priority must be maintained, cost reduction will follow suit. (See Table 7.3.)

It is worth noting here the link between product standardization and rigidity in the production processes. Behind quality looms a requirement for flexibility, the need to keep production processes flexible to give scope for some product customization in order to maintain a competitive difference. The trap to be avoided during the consolidation phase is fighting the battle solely on the grounds of price and cost. By so doing, the organization would be entering a vicious circle: economies of scale leading to overcapacity and increased competition to sell excess production, with the concomitant need to reduce prices and costs further 'to stay in business' by increasing capacity. And this vicious circle goes on: more capacity, increased competition, lower prices, reduced costs, economies of scale, overcapacity, competition, prices ...

Tom Peters (1988, p. 168) quotes the example of a steel mill which, in order to remain flexible, considered its plant as a laboratory. According to Gordon Forward, the founder of Chaparral Steel of Midlothian, Texas, a pioneer in mini-mill technology:

The lab is in the plant ... Of course, we don't give the whole plant over to laboratory work, but the whole plant really is a laboratory – even though it is the most productive steel mill in the world ... We knew we had to stay on top of new technology.

By choosing a strategy of rapidly introducing new products, followed by their withdrawal once they have reached their maturity phase, Hewlett Packard deliberately remains in the fluid stage. It must, therefore, control the innovation process and the two aspects of quality, design and conformity. Texas Instruments, on the other hand, with a strategy of mass production in the solidified stage, must control quality of conformity and improvement. At the outset of their quality revolution, the Japanese opted for quality of conformity and mass production.

Table 7.3

Customization		Standardization
		Production solid phase
Design and development fluid phase		
Introductory stage	Development stage	Maturity stage
Innovation	**Establishment**	**Consolidation**
Strategy of innovation	Strategy of mass production	Strategy of product differentiation
Control of innovation process	Control of industrialization	Control of efficiency and improvement
• Positioning • Development cycle • Number of modifications • Performances • Reliability • Design flexibility	• Machine capability and control of variation • Conformity • Volume and delivery reliability • Volume flexibility	• Improvements (reliability, service, delivery, usage, etc.) • Cost reduction • Productivity improvement • Flexibility of mix
Quality does not prevent innovation and creativity	Quality is maintained despite volume: the objective is to keep the customer loyal	Quality and differentiation are sought in spite of the drive for efficiency

		Rigidity of processes
Flexibility of processes		
		Better-known and mastered technologies
Potential for innovation and differentiation		

Table 7.3 clearly illustrates these three basic quality strategies: a strategy of innovation, a strategy of industrialization and customer retention, a strategy of efficiency and improvement. We will examine them successively.

7.2.3 Quality Deployment in a Strategy of Innovation

A company that chooses a strategy of rapid product introduction must carefully control the innovation process. The importance of prevention and quality planning and control was stressed in Chapter 5 when we dealt with the development of a new product that we considered as a special type of cross-functional process. The quality plan was meant to organize activities such as potential problem analysis, design reviews, verifications and validation.

However, to take the offensive and use quality as a competitive weapon, it is essential at this stage to be more systematic and to engineer and deploy quality during the early stages of creation and development in order to achieve expected requirements.

Managing Risks

What disrupt a project are uncertainties and risks. These uncertainties can come from ill-defined user requirements, from badly structured priorities or from unforeseen changes in the environment. A second category of uncertainties can result from the size of the project or a lack or resources and management support. Finally, technical complexity and lack of expertise in a project team represent a third potential source of uncertainty. To control these risks, management can resort to integration and planning tools.

Customer Integration

In order not to lose track of customer requirements, links can be maintained through customer participation, planned series of meetings, and a formal approval process for specifications or changes.

Cross-functional Co-operation and Agreement

This can be achieved by the location of the multifunctional team on the same geographical site. A multidisciplinary team, interacting like a rugby team, can stimulate innovation, anticipate problems and tackle them in a creative way, and so bring about a substantial reduction of the development cycle (and costs, as development costs are fixed at this stage). It is essential to face contradictions very early and to avoid postponing difficult decisions. Some companies have instituted contract books which contain the collection of agreements. However, other modes of co-operation are possible: a design engineer may be installed in the production department or a quality engineer in the design department. A multidiscipline vision could even be planted in the minds of the engineers through job rotation; for example, an engineer could spend several months in the after-sales department, and then in production before finally settling into the design department.

Choice of Project Manager and Team Members

The experience of the project manager and the level of expertise of the team selected, their participation in the planning of the project and the added training they receive are particularly important if the project presents technological risks.

Planning and Control

Before the quality plan is drawn up, there should be a technical plan to define the user's requirements, the constraints and the quality specifications of intermediate products. But above all the technical plan should define the different stages of the creation process, identify major areas of uncertainty and the different steps of progression: how much prototyping and experimentation, how many activities in parallel, what kinds of linkages and feedback?

To reduce uncertainty, some companies clearly separate the innovation process from the development process. When developing a new product, only approved solutions and tested processes must be used. These solutions are the outcome of the long-term innovation programme.

The quality plan will define the verification strategy: the quality features and levels for the different activities and the control procedures to check that the required level has been achieved. Controls can be formalized and integrated in the development of the activity, or appear at the end as a specific test or design review.

The time and resource plan is based on the work breakdown structure. It represents all necessary activities for the project taken from the technical and quality plan: what should be done, who should do it, who exchanges with whom, and when? The critical path analysis method may be used when the level of uncertainty is not too large.

Quality Function Deployment or Quality Factoring

One of the main risks of project team work is being so technology driven as to lose track of customers' requirements and their evolution. To avoid this, it might be useful to formalize further the customers' needs and 'functions' and control their transcription into technical specifications. This deployment of the basic quality functions and features, from final customers to design, from design to industrial engineering, from industrial engineering to production is known as the quality function deployment method or quality factoring.

The first step is to translate the qualitative requirements and essential functions expected by the customer into final technical and quantified characteristics and specifications. For example, a printer wants paper that does not tear in his machine, but the supplier defines his paper with a series of technical specifications. (See Table 7.4.) The passage from qualitative needs (the 'what') to technical specifications can be represented on a matrix with the question 'How?' and inversely the passage from technical specifications to the customer's needs with the question 'Why?' (See Figure 7.10.)

This line of reasoning can then be extended to the finished product through a series of matrices, running from needs to final characteristics, from final characteristics to component characteristics, from component characteristics to process characteristics, and finally from process parameters to production characteristics and control parameters. (See Figure 7.11.) Each matrix can be used to support a considerable amount of information, as shown in Figure 7.12. Clearly,

Table 7.4

Needs, requirements			Technical specifications or final characteristics				
Main performance functions	Sub-functions	Importance	Thickness	Stiffness	Specific weight	Surface treatment	Etc
Ease of passage through the rotator	No tearing Non-folding	7	×	×	×	×	
		3	×	×			
Quality of print	The paper does not take the ink Etc.	5				×	

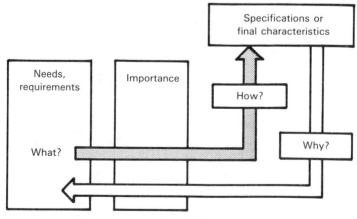

Fig. 7.10

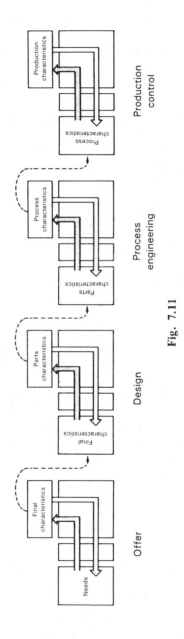

Fig. 7.11

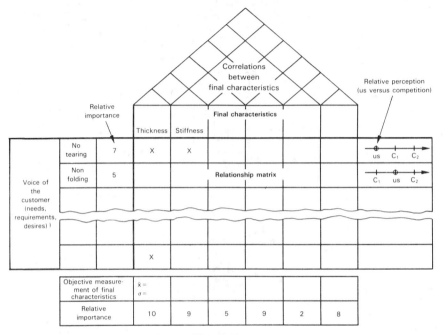

Fig. 7.12

the more structured our knowledge of the product, the more complex and complete will be the matrix. In the initial, creative stages this method can be used as a guide, as an interactive and clarification tool without the need to go into all the details and correlation calculations.

It should be noted that this chain of quality deployment is carried from specification to specification, from customer requirements to the final specification of parts and elementary modules. Specifications can then be tested for internal consistency, and any one of them verified against the preceding one. Conversely, control and test activities should be carried out from the elementary components to the final acceptance test of the delivered product. Each component can be tested for internal consistency, and also verified against its corresponding specification.

7.2.4 Quality Deployment in a Strategy of Establishment and Customer Retention

To establish the product firmly on the market it becomes increasingly important to deliver the offer as promised and just in time; this is the way to keep a loyal customer base and avoid the spread of bad publicity by word of mouth. In the defensive strategy described in the preceding chapters, the offer was based on the specifications drawn up at each phase. But as we are now taking the offensive, the reference is the customers' expectations and perceptions when they use the product. Accordingly, client surveys, customer service and after-sales reports are all vital sources of information, which should immediately be fed back to the production, engineering and design departments.

There is a second difference from the defensive strategy in that now customer satisfaction should be considered as global. Total quality not only means conformity, but also reliable lead times and cost control. However, cost control means cost management and not blind cost cutting, as this reduction results from working on the system, from understanding it better and defining which areas, which linkages should be improved. 'Intelligence' of the system implies an in-depth technical understanding of its operations, and not brute or blind pressure to show results on the bottom line as soon as possible.

Thus, to the quality of conformity approach described in Chapter 5, we are now adding reliability of delivery and cost control. (See Figure 7.13.) Improvements along these three dimensions are inextricably linked, inasmuch as they all aim at fulfilling promises and keeping the customer loyal. Let us consider the linkages that must be reinforced in that strategy.

The simplified block diagram shown in Figure 7.14, similar to the value-added chain described by Porter (1985, Chapter 2), can be used as a basis for the description and comprehension of the various linkages between departments that should be considered. The horizontal boxes represent staff departments supporting line operations, extending from outside suppliers to the final customers.

As already explained, the essential need to maintain quality of conformity and reliability of delivery despite volume build-up makes it necessary to control and improve the system. However, mainly as a result of linkages between departments, new opportunities are now available to improve lead times and productivity. Here are a few examples.

Let us consider the linkage between sales and production. A better knowledge of demand, the better formulation of requirements and more careful order-taking can result in inventory cuts, the elimination of errors and lead time reductions. When a client asks for 100 000 articles, why deliver them all at once and put production under pressure when you know that consumption of that component will be on a regular basis? After all, sudden and large variations in production inevitably lead to extra costs and non-qualities.

Whether in the form of raw materials, work in process or finished products,

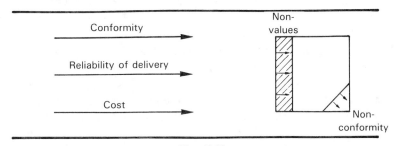

Fig. 7.13

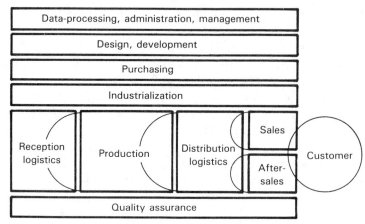

Fig. 7.14

inventories represent a substantial investment throughout the whole production process. Inventories, buffers between sub-systems, may conceal, dampen or distort relevant information. Efforts to smooth flows and achieve just-in-time by reducing the set-up time, or by levelling off demand, are aimed at better quality, better delivery and cost reduction in repetitive manufacturing. All these actions are complementary.

Other linkages are easily imagined. You only have to connect two departments, two boxes as shown in Figure 7.14 to see an opportunity of improvement. In 1983, a careful analysis of a reorganized safety belt fabrication department revealed five areas of progress, representing 62 per cent of the department's added value. (The SPEA case, 1986). The technological transformation represented only 38 per cent of the added value (see Figure 7.15).

7.2.5 Quality Deployment in a Strategy of Consolidation and Differentiation

A product or service usually establishes itself on the market thanks to the novelty of its formula and correct positioning. As time goes by, however, and as the competition begins to make increasing inroads, it loses its originality and becomes increasingly standard. A price reduction based on cost reduction may help it maintain a competitive advantage, but price is not always the determining factor and it may be necessary to use other dimensions to differentiate the product. The choice of the differential therefore becomes a strategic matter, since it is no longer simply a question of inventory reduction, error-free production or waste elimination. This competitive difference should be sought through a careful analysis of the product's competitive position, and the capacities of the firm.

A competitive difference may result from a special advantage the client can obtain from the product. This advantage might appear small or secondary, but if every other dimension is common to all competitors it will be decisive. It may even

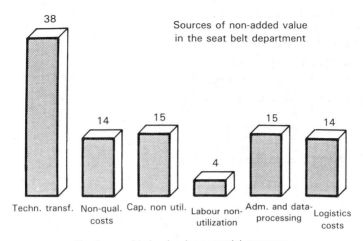

38

Sources of non-added value
in the seat belt department

14   15   15   14

4

Techn. transf. Non-qual. Cap. non util. Labour non- Adm. and data- Logistics
                costs   utilization   processing   costs

% of non-added value by potential progress

Notes:
1. Technological transformation
The series of operations which makes it possible to obtain quality – 'right first time'. This is the only added value the customer is ready to pay for.
2. Improvement areas
Non-quality costs:
Rework, scrap: costs incurred in the manufacturing of defective parts or products – they cover the materials and labour used to manufacture, sort and rework them; the time the machines were used to make the defective products; the energy spent, etc.
Appraisal: inspection and detection costs.
Material waste: this comprises the materials not contained in the finished product (shavings, flash, etc.)
Capacity non-utilization: this relates to the number of machines that are out of order, being adjusted or stopped for tool change, and the personnel, overhead and financial expenses incurred through this loss of potential.
Labour non-utilization: expenses related to absenteeism, accidents at work, social problems, breaks, etc.
Administration and data-processing: this includes administrative functions such as planning, management, etc., also computer data-processing; these costs can be greatly reduced if the preceding costs are reduced.
Logistics costs: this involves overall stocks and materials handling resulting from poor layout and optimization of flows.

Fig. 7.15

be possible to grant it without a price increase, though a price increase can always be justified where extra value is clearly visible. Any superior characteristics can be made visible by linking the user's value chain to the supplier's value chain. Figure 7.16 shows possible linkages leading to competitive advantage. Here are a few examples:

Reduction of the Utilization Cost for the Customer

Linkage between supplier's production and customer's operations: metal sheets are pre-cut by the production department to the dimensions required by the client. The flexibility of the supplier's production facilities leads to savings for the customer in storage cost, cutting operations, inspection, transport, etc.
Linkage between supplier's industrial engineering department and utilization by the customer: the life-cycle cost is reduced by lower operating and maintenance costs (product more robust, more reliable and easy to repair).

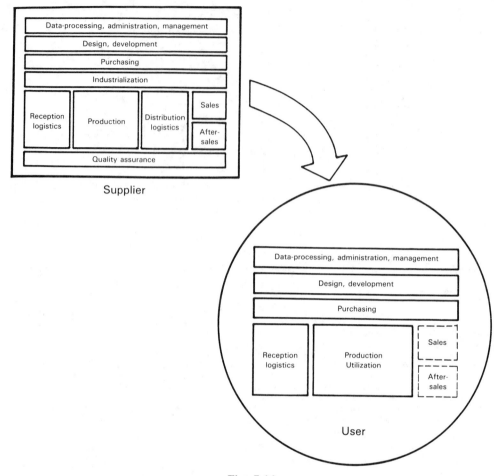

Fig. 7.16

Improved Delivery

Linkage between supplier's production and sales departments and customer's reception logistics: more reliable client demand, electronic data-processing communication, just-in-time delivery, flexibility of supplier's manufacturing processes, etc.

Better Product Performance

Linkage between supplier's engineering design department and user. All quality dimensions can be improved: performance, reliability, maintainability, facility of utilization, of installation, of connection, etc.

Design Facilitation

Linkage between customer and supplier design departments.

- In this, the supplier and his customer are both involved early on in the design of new products. Speaking the same language, together they develop an integrated operational system that will be difficult to break into and beat, even with a price differential.
- By installing computer-assisted design software on the client's premises, a cardboard packaging manufacturer has enabled his customers to design their own packaging. When the client is satisfied with his 'demand' (design, colours, text, all displayed on the screen), he can place an order by simply transferring all the data to his supplier's computer.

All these examples show the importance of knowing, understanding and caring for the customer. Having the right product in the first place is essential, but the 'plus' of service takes on a decisive importance as the product matures.

7.3 EXTERNAL TURNAROUND STRATEGY

Any offensive must be launched from a solidly based and well-defended position. The offensive strategy described in this chapter will, therefore, fall within the same overall framework as the defensive strategy described in Chapter 6.

7.3.1 Management of Change and Leadership

Awareness

The advantage obtained through a better level of conformity will not last forever, and so further differences must constantly be created to maintain perceptible superiority. As the product becomes more standard, these differences are increasingly difficult to create and maintain.

How can we avoid falling into the lethal spiral of standardization, economy of scale, increased capacity, price reduction, overcapacity, price war? The challenge prevents any business from resting on its laurels. The quest for solid, radical superiority naturally begins with innovation, and must then be pursued resolutely as the product is established and consolidated. An analysis of the market and distribution networks can lead to sensitive, decisive differences being identified and selected in the light of the corporation's potential, the positioning of the competition, or changes in technology or the environment. Total quality involves a dynamic adjustment of the product to the targeted segment, and the alignment of the corporation by deploying the voice of the customer internally, with as little distortion as possible.

Everyone should by now have access to the customer, a far more demanding boss than any real manager, and therefore everyone should not only do it right the first time, but do it better the second time in order to make the difference.

Intelligence about the market and the strategic battlefield is not solely built up through managers' opinions or by after-sales reports, but via a host of surveys, studies, benchmarks, direct experiments in the field, listening attentively to the facts and to clients.

The Model: Continuous Improvement

For continuous improvement, the economic, social and cultural approach already described is enlarged to include market and strategic orientation.

Above and beyond innovation (and quality has a role to play in the innovative process itself by introducing greater rigour), continuous improvement is super-imposed on the new and stabilized situation. Product or process innovation is clearly vital for advance via large improvement steps (and here again, quality has a role to play in the innovative process itself) but we should not be content to stabilize and maintain the new situation at its current level; continuous improvement should be superimposed. (See Figure 7.17.)

Continuous improvement has no limit, because the need to adapt and create competitive difference is infinite. However radical the superiority acquired at a given moment, the competition will fight to catch up. Accordingly, the concept of quality becomes general, encompassing every single dimension. Where does quality end? Where does strategy begin? Quality should cover the four production missions: cost/productivity; conformity; delivery (dependability); flexibility. This is perfectly logical inasmuch as all four missions are inextricably interrelated. Improved conformity and delivery result in cost reduction, while flexibility enables faster reaction and better delivery with less inventory and therefore less costs.

The central message of total quality is: learn and work continuously on the system. First work on the conformity dimension, then work on dependability and/or flexibility according to the state of the battlefield. Productivity and cost reduction are ever present as they result from preceding action.

It should be noted that a strategy focusing on conformity to promise achieves the

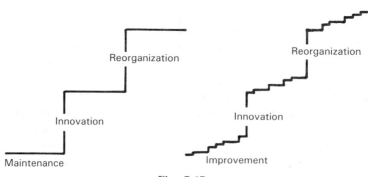

Fig. 7.17

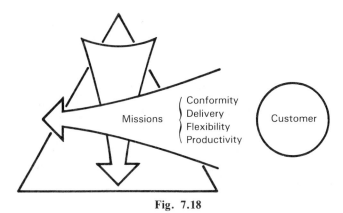

Fig. 7.18

stabilization of the customer base and increased loyalty. With a strategy focusing on a differential advantage, the objective is increased market share. An appropriate marketing strategy can then further product superiority (promotion, price, distribution). However, this superiority will become truly operational only if the entire corporation fully understands its importance and acts accordingly.

As a result of all this, total quality will sweep through the entire firm from top to bottom, cross-functionally with the voice of the customer, and in breadth to cover all missions. Clearly, at this point the meaning of the quality concept becomes too wide to be significant, and it would be preferable to put the emphasis on continuous improvement and learning. (See Figure 7.18.)

A Clear Vision of the Direction to Follow

A defensive strategy based on zero defects or 'doing it right first time' is relatively easy to propagate and explain, though less easy to implement. The concept is simple and can mobilize everyone throughout the firm. For example, it would be easy to launch a campaign based on the five Olympic zeros: zero defects, zero delay, zero inventory, zero breakdown, zero paper – to which could be added zero dispersion.

These overall objectives are relatively independent of the major product positioning decisions. To go further and give a more specific advantage makes it necessary to define the future battlefields and dimensions of superiority. For example, cutting metal sheets directly to the client's requirements instead of selling products at standard dimensions (which would entail another cutting operation by the client) is an important advantage to the user (time saved by direct delivery, lower inventory, better quality, space reduction). This advantage can only be achieved by a clear and disciplined orientation of improvements if costs and investment are to be minimized for the supplier.

Another example is the plasma torch nozzle which wore out very quickly. Any improvement would make a decisive difference to the user, but behind the systematic efforts to develop a radically superior nozzle could lie two years of determined and disciplined developments. The strategic difference as perceived and experienced by the user must be clearly spelt out to get it across to all levels concerned.

Differentiation and improvement proposals travel in both directions: external demands passed on within the corporation and internal opportunities offered to the customer. Proposals and initiatives should both be reintegrated into a strategic direction of the long-term plan.

Top Management Will and Determination

Here again we find the main components already described.

Persuasion
The battle plan has to be explained, as well as the choice of directions for improvement. The situation can be clarified by benchmarking and the presentation of objective facts.

Reassurance and Encouragement
Once the bases have been consolidated, the processes stabilized and quality of conformity assured, going on the offensive to win market share should bring greater job security and profit-sharing.

Providing Resources and Organizing Co-operation
Once the quality programme has been launched, it is essential to maintain the momentum and to feed in projects of increasing significance. As the projects become more strategic, greater account must be taken of the current organization, its leaders and territories. Management must steer change with a clear long-term vision combined with short-term pragmatic and political tactics, for example providing resources for one project, encouraging alliances for another, reorganizing co-operation and promoting champions here, overcoming resistance there. This implies detailed efforts to weave and reweave the fabric of co-operation and exchange.

Knowing and Monitoring Processes
Management by objectives indicates the target to be achieved, and leaves the people in charge to manage the situation and sort it out by themselves. In many circumstances, this approach is valid but not optimal, since once the objective has been reached there is no reason to make further progress. This approach favours and rewards resourceful, inventive and lucky managers.

Total quality, however, presupposes an obstinate striving towards the control and improvement of the system. Accumulated experience counts more than the result at any given time. A manager must, therefore, go beyond given objectives. He must help his subordinates to understand better and become more familiar with their processes, to identify and control the essential parameters governing the result.

Even if he has less ingenious or less talented people under him, with method and discipline they will learn and make progress.

With the continuous improvement philosophy, management cannot merely announce and demand results; it must go into the field and monitor the actual implementation of action and improvement.

7.3.2 Key Elements of the Change Process

This brings us back to the essential roles of the steering committee: monitoring, internal communication, education and recognition.

A Strategic Steering Committee

The role of the steering committee becomes increasingly strategic as the main thrusts of progress are applied in the marketplace. Improvement plans must be harmonized and integrated into strategic plans. The steering committee plays an increasingly institutional role and the choice of its members becomes critical.

Its task is to break down the clearly designated directions for improvement into objectives and sub-objectives, to be carried out via a host of proposals, projects and initiatives coming from the field. The quantified objectives contained in the plan are thus supported by specific actions. The result and timing of these actions must be clearly formalized.

The essential role of the steering committee is, therefore, to monitor the development of the change process by planning it, measuring its progress and co-ordinating actions to promote, educate and recognize merit. Controlling the change process does not merely consist of fixing objectives and pointing out the deviations to be corrected. Controlling the process requires a determination to experiment in order to learn concretely from the field, and to adapt policies and guidelines with pragmatism. Each organization will develop its own quality culture, at its own speed.

Communication and Internal Marketing

Each member of the corporation should have access to the strategic aspect of the business. Decentralization leads to autonomy and well-planned responsibility for performance and improvement. It only remains to re-introduce the customer, that very demanding boss, into the work of everyone in the organization. The new beliefs will value both the outside client and the internal customer in the multiple customer–supplier relationships.

Methods and Education

We have already mentioned quality function deployment (QFD). In addition to the training already described, the employees clearly need a better knowledge of their customers, and why they are doing their job. Everyone should be able to measure the significance of their own work within the overall system.

Recognition of merit and celebration of results

As mentioned in the previous chapter, it is sometimes possible to involve the customer in the recognition process. When promoting a maintenance manager, for example, it is an excellent idea to take account of the opinion of his customers in the production department. Some firms encourage their quality circles or quality improvement teams to go and see their customers.

7.4 IN CONCLUSION

Conformity to requirements is a necessary but not sufficient condition for a firm to survive. What is vital is the customer-driven improvement of the processes and the system throughout the organization, and total quality and continuous improvement enable everyone to align his efforts to achieve the perpetual renewal of strategic differences.

The manner in which this dynamic process is conducted remains highly dependent on the organization and its environment. It is, however, possible to describe the general process that should be followed in order to engineer change, and the classic difficulties that may be encountered on the way. This will be covered in Chapter 10, after dealing with the specificity of services.

Figure 7.19 represents total quality as an element (product relative perceived value) of the marketing mix.

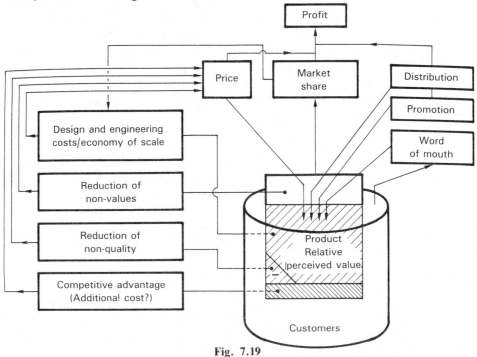

Fig. 7.19

PART III

•

QUALITY IN SERVICES

CHAPTER 8

•

IS THERE A SPECIFIC WAY OF
MANAGING QUALITY IN SERVICES?

The delivery of a service involves direct interaction between the customer and the service delivery system. As a result, the quality perceived by a customer is different from that of a manufactured product. A service is, however, often accompanied by a physical element, something tangible, made elsewhere, such as a meal prepared in the kitchen of a restaurant. Conversely, the delivery of an industrial product can include services, the quality of which is of no little importance.

Where then, lies the difference? In order to define this difference, it is essential to start with an operational definition of a service which will be both helpful to management and easily transferable from the industrial situation to the service area.

8.1 AN OPERATIONAL DEFINITION OF A SERVICE

A service is essentially characterized by its interface, that is, the place where the interaction between a customer and the delivery system takes place. Clearly, the customer is physically present in this interface area, and production and consumption are simultaneous. This simultaneity places the consumer directly within the production process. The interface area is often complemented by a 'support' area, in which the physical handling or processing necessary to the delivery of the service itself takes place, i.e. writing up documents, transactions, handling files, laboratory analysis, the preparation of meals. In comparing this with industrial production, certain authors term the whole process 'servuction' (Eiglier and Langeard, 1987), a strange hybrid between service and production. Figure 8.1 shows the basic diagram.

Whether the transaction with a customer involves a service or a manufactured product, the interface and the support are always separate. But whereas with a service, dealings with the customer take place essentially at the interface area, with an industrial product, production occurs in the 'support' area – that is the factory – in the absence of the customer. Consequently, the difference between a service and an industrial product is merely a difference of degree. (See Figure 8.2.)

Managing a service means, above all, managing the interface. Managing the

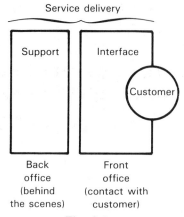

Fig. 8.1

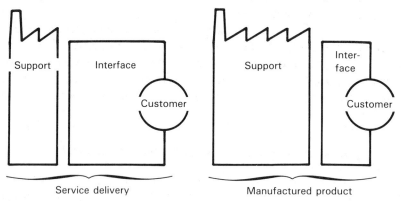

Fig. 8.2

manufacture of a product, by contrast, means managing the support or the plant. As the following examples demonstrate, these two modes of management are very different.

8.1.1 The Restaurant Example

A restaurant is composed of a dining room which is the interface area, the place where the service is delivered and consumed, and a kitchen which is the support area, the place where the meals are prepared. The dining room is customer orientated, the kitchen is production orientated. These two very different logics, each with their own very different priorities, often lead to conflict between the interface and the support, the dining room and the kitchen, the waiters and the 'chefs'.

This interface–support organization can take various forms according to which customer segment is being targeted and which formula is chosen. Take, for example, three different types of restaurant: the traditional restaurant, the Benihana restaurant and the McDonald-style fast-food restaurant, shown in Figure 8.3.

We note that in the Benihana restaurant, the enlargement of the interface through the transfer of part of the support to the interface makes for more visible

Classical restaurant

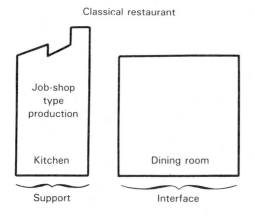

In a classical restaurant a conflict exists between waiters in the dining room who are mainly customer-orientated and the chef and his production team who are mainly preoccupied with meal preparation and scheduling.

Benihana restaurant

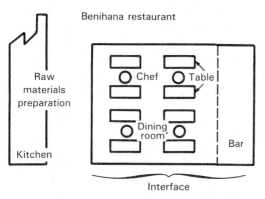

In a Benihana restaurant customers waiting at the bar are brought to the hibachi table in 'batches' of eight. The chefs cook and serve directly in the dining room. Each chef is responsible for two tables of eight. The kitchen is small as the raw materials preparation is simple and standard.

In a fast-food restaurant, the dining room is simple but clean. The interface is extremely reduced in a drive-in formula. On the other hand there are production lines and a large work-force in the kitchen.

Fig. 8.3

interaction, and hence more 'real' service. However, managing the interface may be more difficult and costly, because managing direct interaction with the customer is always more complex and uncertain than managing materials in the support area. Here, the extra cost is compensated for by intensive utilization of the chefs and of the facilities.

In the fast-food restaurant we see the opposite movement. The standardization of the product goes hand-in-hand with the standardization and simplification of the interface, which consequently becomes smaller or simpler. In the support area, the industrial logic of the standardized product leads to production lines.

8.1.2 The Bank Example

At a bank counter, the clerk provides certain services which the customer consumes on the spot; the cashing of cheques, deposit transactions, information. This is the interface sector: the front office. However, not every transaction can be completed intermediately, and so the customer's request is often transformed into paper. This intermediate document is then dealt with in the support area 'behind the scenes', both in the literal and figurative sense: the back office. There, the information is processed in the usual manufacturing style with work stations and intermediate storage (work in process).

8.1.3 Air Transport Example

During a flight from Paris to New York, the passenger travels in the plane, inside the transport-producing instrument. The passenger is consuming travel at the same time as the company is producing it, and a time interval between production and consumption cannot even be imagined. During the journey, therefore, the passenger is directly involved in the production process. Furthermore, both in the plane and at the airport the passenger is only vaguely aware of the support systems which take over from the interactive systems: luggage, maintenance, air-traffic control, preparation of meals, etc.

In the last two examples, interactions are multiple: travelling by plane, for example, involves first contact with the travel agency, followed by reservation by telephone, booking-in, contact with the air stewardess or steward, transfer and the collection of luggage. Each one of these contacts is a 'moment of truth' to use the expression of Jan Carlzon (1987, p. 3), President of Scandinavian Airlines System.

> Last year, each of our 10 million customers came in contact with approximately five SAS employees, and this contact lasted an average of 15 seconds each time. Thus SAS is 'created' 50 million times a year, 15 seconds at a time. These 50 million 'moments of truth' are the moments that ultimately determine whether SAS will succeed or fail as a company.

8.2   A DIFFERENCE OF DEGREE

As these examples show, the interactive or 'pure service' part can vary considerably. Therefore, instead of making too general statements about the activity sector where the distinction between service and production is hazy, we will turn to the delivery system, where the definition put forward earlier is more operational.

We can, then, say that every activity is partly service or interface and partly production or support. It is the proportional importance of these two blocks within an activity which will make the service aspect of the activity more or less pronounced. If the interface is large and essential, the activity should be classified as service. If the support is dominant, the activity should be classified as manufacturing or industry. It is even possible to illustrate the link between these two blocks by a ratio of service intensity such as:

$$\text{Service intensity} = \frac{\text{cost of interface (people + machines)}}{\text{total cost (interface + support)}}$$

$$\text{or} \quad \frac{\text{added value of interface}}{\text{total added value}}$$

When dealing with interactive and project-orientated service (consultancy for example), the indication can be expressed as:

$$\text{Service intensity} = \frac{\text{man hours spent with client}}{\text{total man hours}}$$

With the development of automation, many industrial firms are clearly enlarging the service dimension of their activity. Let us analyze the specificity of the interface sector.

8.3   SERVICE SPECIFICITY OF THE INTERFACE

8.3.1   Service and Process Cannot be Separated in the Interface – They Occur Simultaneously

The consequences are as follows:

1. The product is the process, the process is the product.
2. A service cannot be stored. A non-consumed service is lost. This is the case if a hotel room or an aeroplane seat is not used. If capacity exceeds demand the unused part is wasted, but if capacity is insufficient the customer is stored in a waiting line or lost. This is one of the main problems in the service sector – how to balance demand and capacity?
3. A service is relatively intangible. It is difficult to protect a service by a patent or by a notion of ownership. It is also difficult to demonstrate a service. Therefore one must try to make a service tangible so that it is more accessible (samples, pictures, brochures, description of facilities, etc.)

4. The moment of truth. A service is the result of a series of 'moments of truth'. Each moment is made up of multiple interactions which are difficult to control from the outside. The employee, for example, is responsible for his interactions, hence the importance of doing it right first time and adjusting to customer demand while delivering the service. Once the service has been delivered, it is very difficult to take corrective action (recovery).

5. Importance of experience versus other modes of communication. Owing to the fact that a service is relatively intangible, modes of communication such as the traditional media have far less impact than those of direct perception or of word of mouth (reputation, rumours). The success of a film is largely explained by this phenomenon. This is the basis of customer loyalty.

8.3.2 The Client is Physically Present

The consequences are as follows:

6. Variety and volatility of requirements. Not only may expectations vary from one customer to another, one customer may even change his mind at any given moment, according to the intensity of the interaction or the circumstances (business or leisure for example). The different names used for a client bring to light the wide variety of roles, and the need to define them: for example, a user, subscriber, subject, citizen, beneficiary, onlooker, taxpayer, number, patient, sick person, guest, visitor.

7. The customer's perception of quality is global. A service is the result of a series of 'moments of truth' experienced by the customer, who then expresses his satisfaction in a global manner: 'I do like doing my shopping there' or 'Oh – I never go there…I don't like it.' In the latter case, it is useful to ask 'Why not?' in order to trace back to the origin of the dissatisfaction. This often stems from something which is of little importance by itself, but which tarnishes the general impression.

8. The customer can participate. By participating, the customer may use his own experience or know-how. He may also wish to take over the situation or save time. We may therefore say that a customer can be partly considered as an employee. Although customer participation introduces an additional element of uncertainty, it may lead both to a reduction in personnel costs and to an improvement in quality control. The customer can also play an important role by giving opinion on the way the service is designed and developed.

9. A network becomes essential. Because a service is realized in the presence of the consumer, there are no channels of distribution as there are for a manufactured product. Hence, there is a need for a network of agencies, chains of restaurants or stores, and for new developments aimed at improving the transportability of a service (information networks).

CHAPTER 9

·

QUALITY AT THE INTERFACE

From our definition of a service, two very different modes of quality management can be distinguished. They are the management of the moments of truth in the interface area, and the management of the tangible in the support area. In the latter case, whether it is a money transaction taking place in the back office at the bank, a blood analysis in the laboratory or the preparation of a hamburger in the kitchen, the conventional methods used for a manufactured object will apply. As these methods have already been dealt with earlier, we will now focus on quality within the interface area, the pure and intangible part of the service delivery. This demands a specific mode of management.

The definition of quality brings us back to our dual articulation: on the one hand the positioning of the service offered over the target market segment and the search for a competitive edge, on the other delivery of the offer in full conformity. We will now look at these two aspects in greater detail.

9.1 COMPETITIVE POSITIONING OF THE SERVICE: QUALITY OF DESIGN

The definition of a homogeneous segment of potential customers can be achieved through the use of demographic or socio-professional characteristics (age, income, occupation). However, given the fact that the customer is directly involved in the delivery process, psychosociological characteristics (the way customers think and behave) are more important. These may include, for example, utilization characteristics like business or leisure, or locality characteristics like place of work. In each segment the customers have common needs, wants and expectations that are specific to this target. What could these needs be?

9.1.1 The Needs

The list of needs is long, for not only is the sought after performance important, for example, the actual transport from one place to another within a given time or a successful surgical operation, but the fact that consumption and production are simultaneous also makes the way the service is performed and delivered essential. The visible and perceived 'how' counts for quite as much as the 'what'. (See Figure 9.1.) Thus the list of the needs to be satisfied starts with the performance itself, covers the way the customer is taken care of and includes trust, friendliness, etc.

These needs may be classified according to the Maslow hierarchy: primary needs, the need to feel secure, to belong, to feel esteemed, to grow and develop (see Figure 6.4). They can also be classified according to the four basic interactions of the moments of truth:

● Interaction with the service delivery process: response time, accessibility, etc.
● Interaction with the technology or with the premises: layout, comfort, availability of equipment, etc.
● Interaction with employees or managers: welcome, friendliness, spontaneity, etc.
● Interaction with other customers: convivial participation, exchange of experience, etc.

Our classification which follows and draws its inspiration from the two preceding

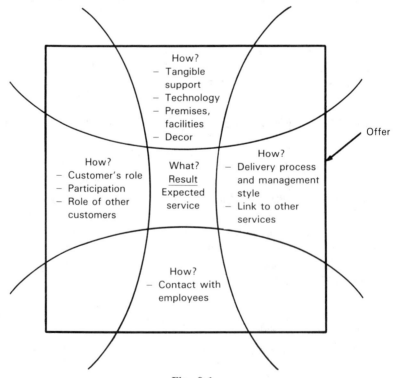

Fig. 9.1

observations, is as arbitrary as any other. But it should lead to reflection and prompt the memory to make sure nothing important is forgotten.

Quality of Result

1. Functional characteristics and performances: the 'What'
   - customization–standardization
   - compatibility with other services.

Quality in the Process

2. Response time
   - promptness
   - cycle time.

3. Ease of access
   - convenient location
   - convenient hours
   - queues not too long
   - user friendly.

4. Tangibles
   - premises, environment
   - decor, uniforms, costumes
   - comfort, cleanliness, luxury
   - technology, equipment.

Quality of Conformity

5. Reliability, consistency
   - results as promised (standards)
   - everything works
   - punctuality
   - accurate and timely information.

Quality of Interaction

6. Diagnosis, responsiveness, recovery
   - listening, availability, understanding
   - adapted response, problem solving
   - explanations, communication, education
   - global treatment, follow-up.

⁷. Empathy, consideration
- courtesy, respect, tact, signs of recognition, use of names
- the customer is important, a guest not a tourist
- good faith is recognized.

Emotional Quality

8. Assurance
- trust, reassurance, minimum risk and discord, safety, guarantee
- explanations, preparation, education
- fair treatment, follow-up
- guarantee of result.

9. Positive experience
- spontaneity
- convivial, at ease, part of the group
- autonomy, opportunity to contribute, to control the situation.

9.1.2 Important Dimensions, Determinant Dimensions

Some of the above dimensions will be taken into consideration when defining the offer. Some of them are obvious, such as safety or the price of a ticket in air transport, but although these are important dimensions they are not necessarily determinant. There are others which may seem secondary, but can make all the difference. These determinant dimensions are the 'pluses' that will decide customers to buy your service.

For example, for their 'Euroclass' service, the Scandinavian Airlines System targeted the frequent business traveller. On top of the more basic needs, these travellers appreciate the frequency of flights (response time), the welcome given by the stewards or stewardesses, the availability of a telephone or a microcomputer in-flight. It is these secondary dimensions that make the difference to them, for safety is a must for all airlines. Thus, when an airline company positions its offer, it must not only cover the important dimensions provided by most other airlines, but also offer a plus, a competitive advantage.

To summarize, the quality of design is first of all the ability to adjust the offer to the requirements of the target market segment. Give the customer the right service, the one that interests him or her and that he or she can perceive is right. Do not provide services customers do not need or want (such as an over-abundant meal) for such extraneous offers will not be positively perceived. They will fall into that part of the square lying outside the circle, as illustrated in Figure 9.2.

Secondly, the quality of design is the plus that makes the difference, the competitive advantage such as punctuality. We have seen how wide the range of requirements can be in the interface, and how great the potential for creating this

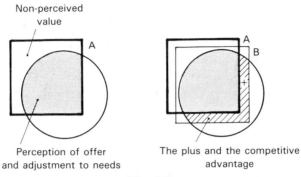

Fig. 9.2

difference. But remember, promises must be kept. Thus our next step is quality of conformity, doing the service right (section 9.2 of this chapter).

9.1.3 Strategies for Adjusting the Offer

After the service concept has been positioned in the market segment to give more value at the same or lower cost, quality of design implies increasing customer perception. According to how this adjustment is to be performed, one of three principal strategies may be chosen:

1. Strategies for adjusting the offer to give more perceived value.
2. Strategies for preparing customers' expectations and adjusting demand.
3. Strategies for enhancing perception during delivery.

Design the Offer to Increase Perceived Value

The following principles should serve as guide lines:

First Principle: Focus Processes
The more homogeneous the target market segment, the more simple and controllable the delivery will be. We know that a production process cannot be

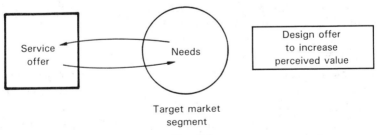

Fig. 9.3

optimized on all evaluation criteria. Standardization of the service, for example, leads to low costs but reduced quality of perception and greater rigidity. It is therefore important to assign clear missions to the delivery processes. If you decide to enlarge the interface, to increase flexibility or give more value, you cannot at the same time expect to please another segment of customers who want a more standardized service at lower cost. The delivery system should then be divided into smaller and more effective sub-systems, each well focused on clear missions.

Second Principle: A Simple and Coherent Formula
In the interface, the product is the process and the process is the product. This fact makes it essential to adjust the service and its delivery system simultaneously. On the other hand, the customer is going to experience a series of moments of truth, like the patient in a hospital being transported from one service to another, or the student going from a class in marketing to one in production. He or she is expected to integrate the series of interactions or moments of truth. To increase the perception of quality, some coherence must be carefully built in, and the offer should remain simple, easy to understand and communicate. Thinking too big, giving too much, adding multiple secondary services to the basic service, all these risk causing a loss of coherence, so that the promised quality is not delivered.

In some services, contact with the clients is rather diffuse: contact for example could involve three different services – sales force, customer service and maintenance (a dealership for example). Any effort to co-ordinate the relationship with the customer will have a high pay off. Sometimes the interface is minimum. In the telephone or the electricity services, the interaction is reduced to the telephone, the plugs and the bills or complaints received by the customer service. It is important, therefore, to co-ordinate these moments of truth carefully.

Third Principle: Interface Versus Support
The interaction in the interface enhances customer satisfaction, even though quality of conformity is more difficult to obtain and control. In the Benihana restaurant example in Chapter 8 the interface has been enlarged. The customers wait comfortably at the bar before making their way to a hibachi table where they are immediately served by the chef himself. The kitchen (support system) is reduced to a minimum. The fact that the food is rather standardized is compensated for by the rather exotic decor, the sophisticated preparation and the entertainment. The customer gets more perceived value, even though costs are lower.

Fourth Principle: Decentralization and Flexible Adjustment
Despite the care taken to select and educate customers, their behaviour remains unpredictable in the interface. Given the multiple interactions this adds to the possible variations of the delivery process, and makes it impossible to define instructions and standards for all possible situations. Moreover, the customer often expects a certain amount of customization and spontaneity from the

employee. Another factor here is the need to give employees the freedom to deal with any problem and put things right, without first having to report back through the hierarchy for approval. Employees should, therefore, be free to act, adjust their behaviours or make decisions within the framework of clear, measurable standards and directives coherent with the final characteristics of the offer. This will give employees an opportunity to recover any loss of service and reduce the response time. 'A good recovery can turn angry, frustrated customers into loyal ones. It can, in fact, create more goodwill than if things had gone smoothly in the first place' (Hart *et al.*, 1990).

Standards, procedures and regulations descending from the hierarchy should be kept to a minimum, and improved through employee participation. According to Jan Carlzon (1986, p. 195) it is a question of turning the pyramid upside down (see Figure 9.4):

> Customers should be at the top, then come the front line people in direct contact with them. Front line people are to be supported by the other functions who operate behind the scenes. Management is then supporting the preceding tiers.

We did not turn the pyramid upside down in this diagram but we put it on its side to follow the flow logic from customers to interface and to support and emphasize the back-up role of management.

Fifth Principle: Value Analysis and Cost Reduction in the Interface

Enlarging the interface means giving more value. But how much will all this cost? The interface usually costs more than the support, due to the fact that interactive service tends to be more customized, that there is direct contact with the employee and that capacities are frequently poorly utilized (the utilization rate of facilities must remain distinctly inferior to 1 if queues are not to become too long). However

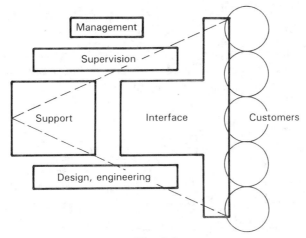

Fig. 9.4

there are many ways of giving more value while reducing cost. For example:

- Increase customer perception without higher costs, or perhaps even reduced ones. The Benihana example cited previously is a good illustration of this. Customer perception can be reinforced by making the service more tangible (see section on this in 'Enhance perception during delivery' below).
- Optimize utilization of existing capacities. Buffer stock of customers at the input to fully utilize capacity. Introduce more flexibility through part-timers or multifunctional personnel.
- Reinforce customer participation in service delivery (see section on this in 'Enhance perception during delivery' below).
- Leverage professionals or costly resources: implement expert systems to share knowledge in the interface; secretaries and nurses do the administrative work, or carry out the simple tasks of doctors, freeing them for more professional activities.
- Simplify activities, suppress tasks with no added value for the client.
- Automate standardized tasks.
- Transfer certain tasks from the interface to the support.

Prepare Customers' Expectations and Adjust Demand

Once the offer has been defined, it is communicated to the customer and induces expectations. If the expectations were higher than those the customer actually perceives, the result will be disappointment. If, on the other hand, perception exceeds expectations, the customer will experience greater satisfaction. Once again, however, we must emphasize that customers can only know what a service is really worth once they have experienced it. Accordingly, they will look for clues (tangible clues, price, references, word-of-mouth, expert advice, etc.) that will help them decide and bring reassurance.

The Traditional Media
Advertisements, signs, samples, descriptions, sales representatives' advice, etc., all induce expectations. However, the role of the media is not only to promise something, it must also explain, reassure, educate.

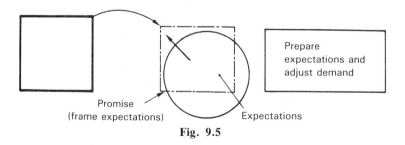

Promise
(frame expectations)

Expectations

Prepare expectations and adjust demand

Fig. 9.5

The Price

The price, of course, indicates the level of service to be expected. At one extreme there is the snob effect and ostentatious service, at the other, the paltriness of some services offered by certain public organizations. But even if price is an important dimension, it is not always determinant.

Former Experience and Word of Mouth

Real experience and word of mouth can have a much greater impact than the traditional media. Customer expectation can be built up through former experience. The success of a new film will depend more on word of mouth, or on a favourable review by an expert than on its advertising. Sponsorship may be used (Alan Prost for car accessories, for example), as well as references, other customers' testimony, or a more direct form of communication may be facilitated through user clubs, fan clubs, 'war' veterans or alumni meetings.

Location

Quality of service, promotion and price, are the first three elements of the marketing mix, the fourth is place or location. But as we have observed, in services there are no distribution channels as there are for industrial products. The service is delivered within the interface area and consumed on the spot, which means it must be located close to the customer. It should not be overlooked that the choice of site can play a very important role when adjusting demand.

Adjusting demand

The service promise should correspond to normal delivery conditions. If demand is higher than capacity, the result may be a deterioration of the service observable, for example, in queues. In this case, if capacity is not flexible enough, it is important to modify the demand, to filter it, to shift it or level it off (advance booking, on- and off-season prices and advantages, etc.).

Enhance Perception During Delivery

The Perception Map

Inside our head, each one of us has a perception map, the outcome of many years

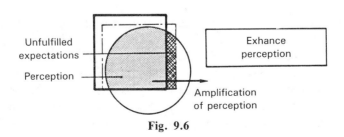

Fig. 9.6

of education, culture and experience. This map has its own specific landscape, and just as streams flow towards valleys to join rivers, so the impressions and perceptions on our perception maps move according to acquired patterns, following a geography outlined by experience. The customer's perception of an offer is filtered by this map, a fact that should be recognized and understood before any attempt to influence a customer is made.

Perception maps are often difficult to change. For example, fish on a bed of ice is always taken as a sign of freshness, even though objectively it is a poor method of preservation.

Lessening Perception of Risk and Uncertainty
When customers have to wait, explain what is going on, show that things are under control. We have noted earlier the importance of service recovery. A good recovery can transform the perception.

Taking Special Care of First Impressions and Reputation
Once an impression has been formed it remains firmly rooted in the customer's mind, and all additional information will tend to reinforce this first impression: after all, seeing is believing. If one expects good service, one will tend to minimize the negative points. This is why the image, the reputation, the first contact, the first impression are all absolutely essential when offering a service.

Integrating all Interactions and Paying Attention to Details
In the customer's mind, sequences of interactions and moments of truth are synthesized to form a global impression of satisfaction. Customers integrate these moments, and assemble their different impressions into a global picture, which just one negative element can ruin. For example, just by being seen wearing a stained white coat, a doctor could tarnish his or her reputation, while an uncomfortable seat can make a good film seem less riveting. How many positive impressions will then be needed to make up for a single minus?

Reinforcing the Perception by Making the Service More Tangible
The simultaneity of production and consumption, as we have emphasized, tends to make a service intangible. Therefore any material or tangible elements may become important, as it can give perceptible signals that may help anticipate the quality of the service.

The façade of a bank may give an impression of solidity. The label on a bottle may give the impression that the wine is going to be excellent, whereas a bar code on the same label could have the opposite effect.

The origin of these tangible elements can be very diverse: decor, technology (computers, X-ray facilities, etc.), uniforms, brochures, pamphlets, dossiers, reports full of figures and exhibits, demonstration materials, samples – even customer loyalty or membership cards can play their part here. We can refer again to the Benihana restaurant:

> The steaks are trimmed in-house. Only a bit of fat at the tail is left, and this is for effect. When the chef begins cooking the meat, he dramatically trims this part off and pushes it aside before cubing the remaining meat.

Reinforcing Customer Participation and Employee Freedom of Action

When customers participate in the creation of a service, in its delivery or its control, they use their personal know-how to influence the process. The fact that they are 'one of us' and have some credibility makes their perceptions all the more positive.

In the same way, perceptions may be influenced by the availability of the employee. On questioning its clientele, British Airways discovered the importance of 'spontaneity'. Customers preferred spontaneous interactions with employees, such as improvised announcements on the plane, rather than standardized exchanges or announcements learnt by heart.

9.2 DELIVERY OF THE SERVICE: QUALITY OF CONFORMITY

Although the service delivery system is now well defined through standards and specified characteristics, giving the right service is not enough. The customer also wants the service right and defect-free. This will be more easily achieved if, right from the start, the formula is simple and easy to communicate at each level of interaction.

Defect-free does not mean perfection. It means delivering the offer in conformity with expectations and standards. And it should be remembered that a simple 'minus' (a defect, problem, a discrepancy between perception and expectation) will have a far greater impact than the many 'pluses' that have been added to make the offer more attractive. The slightest doubt about the safety of the plane you are flying in will immediately cancel out any pleasure you might get from the smiles of the stewardesses and stewards or the large drinks being served.

It may take many pluses to compensate for a minus on the customer's perception map. We memorize our frustrations far better than our satisfaction. Moreover, it is a fact that we talk about our bad experiences more; on average we may tell five times more people about a negative experience than a positive one.

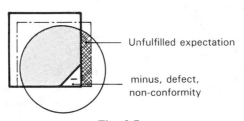

Fig. 9.7

Quality of conformity is thus essential, which brings us back to the classical approach described for product manufacturing, only this time with the emphasis on quality of conformity within the interface. Everything starts with standards and measurable goals. Clearly, measurements must be customer-orientated, and excuses for not making them so are even less acceptable when the customer is physically present. We are thus back to the three main lines of action: plan; do and check (i.e. maintain); act (i.e. improve).

9.2.1 Planning Quality into the Delivery System

The service concept, designed and adjusted, has now to be delivered at the interface to give the 'what' and the 'how' as promised. How will specifications, standards, operating procedures be validated? These concern the equipment and technology, the delivery process and the layout, the role of employees and even the role of customers. In order to guarantee the performance, the delivery system should be made as robust as possible by anticipating and preventing potential problems. The advice given in the preceding chapters is fully applicable here, with the following particularities:

Pilot Projects and 'Prototyping'

Rather than spending too much time on design and market studies, it is usually better to go ahead with pilot projects, as these tend to give concrete expression to the service as a whole. The more immaterial the service, the more important this expression becomes. Chains of shops and restaurants are more often than not the follow-up to pilot projects or successful 'prototypes'.

Capacity Analysis at Peak Level

Quality of delivery is dependent on service attendance. At peak levels, queues and bottlenecks may appear, making quality problems more acute and visible.

Coherence Analysis

A customer involved in a service offer is different from a mechanical component involved in a production process. A customer may feel annoyed at the breaking up of an operation and any resulting delay. This is why it is important to plan the production process as a whole, and represent the succession of interactions experienced by the customer on a flow chart.

When a service is made up of numerous interactions involving many different employees, each may tend to do his job in his own way. As a result, the need to have someone or some way of supervising the cycle in its totality may be overlooked. It is therefore important to review the series of interactions experienced by the customer, in order to build positive coherence into the customer satisfaction. This integration can sometimes be realized by designating a co-ordinator who will 'own' and develop the cross-functional service. It can also be done by enlarging and enriching jobs.

An Autonomous and Responsible 'Front Line'

Giving people autonomy and responsibility often necessitates a reorganization of jobs and functions (enlargement, enrichment) and the promotion of team work. It is the 'interface' or 'front line' people that make quality possible. Therefore, the more customers' demands and needs vary, or the more the environment fluctuates, the more employees need freedom of action and the less effective they will be under conditions imposing a heavy hierarchy or rigid standards. By allowing employees to correct problems that come into their sphere of responsibility without referring to various hierarchical levels, it is possible to simplify operating procedures and shorten hierarchies. Given the complexity of the interaction, standards cannot cover every facet, so a lot of responsibility will have to remain with the employees; hence the importance of their selection and training.

Building Quality Through Careful Selection and Training of Personnel

A service company's most valuable asset is its personnel, which means that the quality of the result will depend to a large extent on the recruitment, training and retaining of this asset. Investing in prevention means investing in recruitment and training. Clearly the people needed in the interface should be predisposed towards social interaction, and sufficiently assertive to take decisions and solve problems as they arise.

At Disney World, every new recruit including the park sweepers go through three days' training. Training people to use a broom obviously does not take three days; most of that time is actually spent in learning how Disney World functions and how to reply, in a courteous and precise manner, to the host of questions that visitors or 'guests' may ask.

Building Quality Through Careful Selection and Training of Customers

In any service, the primary raw material is the customer. This makes it important to encourage control and selection at entry level; if the variety of customers entering the process is too wide, the quality will deteriorate. At the Shouldice Hospital, a clinic specializing in hernia operations, only 'customers' in 'good health' are admitted (they fill in a questionnaire and undergo a medical examination). There is thus little risk of complications during or following the operation. The length of the operation is stable, the use of the operating rooms is optimized, the flow is regular and performance, measured by the recurrence rate of hernia, is quite high.

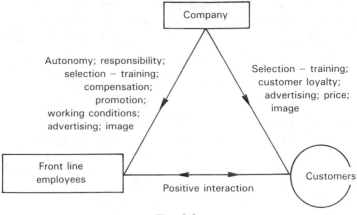

Fig. 9.8

Although customers can be considered as the primary raw material, they are not lifeless. They can be trained and educated, they can participate. At the Shouldice Hospital, patients are prepared for their operation in three different ways: through written explanations, explanations given by the nursing staff and, after dinner on the day they arrive, through interaction with patients who have just undergone the operation. Later on, the hospital provides annual check-ups for its 'alumni', free of charge. These occur at the time of the annual reunion (dinner and floor show), attended by former patients.

A club is an excellent way of transforming former or loyal customers into salespeople. New members are initiated and trained as they socialize and exchange experiences.

In summary, it is often relevant to put customers and employees on the same level. This relationship is represented by the triangle in Figure 9.8, which links customers and employees to the company in a balanced way. This parallel treatment of customers and employees can be illustrated by communications and advertisements that target the employee as much as the external customer. This can apply equally to facility layout, staff uniforms or working conditions. Rocky Aioki, manager of the Benihana restaurant network, places great importance on the fact that his restaurants are built using authentic Japanese materials. This is as important for the Japanese chefs, who enjoy working in an authentic setting, as it is for the customers.

9.2.2   Delivering and Maintaining Consistent Quality

Quality must be consistently delivered, day after day, and promised levels of service must be maintained throughout the network.

Process Control

Statistical process control, applied to a manufactured product, consists of carefully monitoring the evolution of the key parameters which condition the final result. If, at the level of methods, machines, materials, manpower and environment the right conditions are met, then the final results will be right the first time.

This philosophy can be equally applied to services, for the interface is made up of moments of truth which have to be right first time. These moments of truth are conditioned by the four-sided interactions between the employees, the facilities, the delivery process and the other customers. Quality of conformity can be achieved through goals, standards, procedures and behaviours that are clearly set out or learned. The real difficulty lies in the fact that the points to be supervised are both numerous and diverse: answer the phone within 20 seconds, serve hamburgers that are less than seven minutes old, maintain cleanliness by hourly checks, follow a 'welcome' etiquette, look at the customer and smile, – dozens of standards and procedures for a service as simple as that of a McDonald's restaurant.

Customer Control, Filtering and Orientation at Entry Point

At the entrance to the manufacturing process of an industrial product, raw materials are carefully inspected to ensure flawless production. This control is far more complex in a service, for at the entrance to the interface, customer behaviour is relatively unpredictable and variable.

Employees must, therefore, know how to adapt their service to the situation, educate the customer if necessary or solve unexpected problems. This positive behaviour will generate a positive reaction from customers, who will feel that they are being listened to. This is the virtuous circle of interaction. In the same way, a series of reciprocal negative interactions will lead to a vicious circle that can cancel out the positive preparation for the encounter.

The quality of filtering and orientation at the entry point is an essential aspect both for improving productivity (better focus of delivery system, better and regular use of capacity) and for controlling the consistency and the quality of the service to be provided.

Quality Control by Management

The careful selection and training of personnel is a preventive measure. It is, in fact, difficult for management to supervise the behaviour of its personnel during the delivery of the service, during every single moment of truth. Accordingly, management supervision should concentrate on those factors which condition the service (standards, procedures, key variables) and on the customer perception, which can be ascertained through performance measurement and feedback (indicators, questionnaires, surveys, complaints, etc.). The employees themselves must be made aware of their direct responsibility, and their efforts and results focused accordingly.

The less management is able to supervise the moments of truth, the more its role of supporter (organization of process, definition of standards and operation modes), of trainer and adviser becomes essential. By emphasizing good results they communicate the standards. By using complaints they can discuss improvements. (See Figure 9.9.)

After selection at entry level and direct control by employees and management, the quality of the service provided is best controlled by the customers themselves.

Direct Control by Customers

As we have already noted, customers and employees should be treated in a similar way. Customers should be considered as employees and employees as customers. Customers may thus be considered responsible for quality in the same way as the employees who serve them. The role and participation of customers can be reinforced by making them aware of the measurement systems, by making the various interactions highly visible and by reminding them of the level of quality they should expect.

Control by Colleagues and Peers

Peer influence can be exercised through team work and training.

Surveys and Audits

Quality delegation to employees and customers does not mean that quality assurance, in the form of audits and surveys, can be dispensed with. It is important to monitor customer satisfaction over a lengthy period of time and, in case of

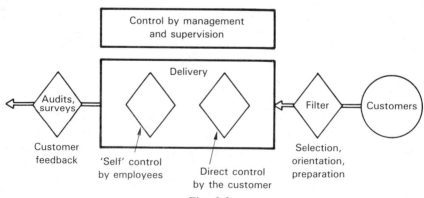

Fig. 9.9

dissatisfaction, to ask why. This will make it possible to trace the reasons back through the process. Posting the results for employees to see on a notice board will enhance self-control.

9.2.3 Improving

It has by now become clear that management is no longer merely responsible for achieving fixed objectives, as was the case in the good old days of management by objectives. Managers are not only expected to reach objectives but to improve them. In order to widen the gap with the competition, the service must be constantly improved and renewed, project by project. None of this, however, differs from what we described in manufacturing. So what are the particular features of improvement in the interface?

Quality Circles with Front Line Personnel

In the interface, things are not as simple as in industry because front line employees are in direct contact with customers. These employees are able to comprehend directly both the needs and the satisfaction level of the customer they are serving. It is therefore possible to work on improvement in two directions: horizontally, via cross-functional groups and quality circles involving front line people, from customer to support; and vertically, via classical improvement teams within departments, top down and bottom up.

Network Validation

The interface personnel are frequently scattered throughout a network of agencies, hotels, restaurants, offices, etc., and solutions that have been found to be effective in one place cannot necessarily be implemented in every part of the network. This makes the introduction of a validation procedure important, so that local solutions can be improved and accepted by the network as a whole. The approval committee should include interface employees, so that real contact is maintained between the home office and its agencies. (See Figure 9.10.)

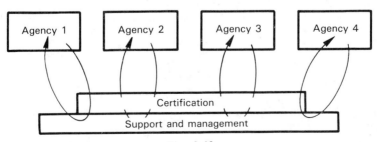

Fig. 9.10

PART IV

•

THE CHANGE PROCESS:
METHODOLOGY AND TOOLS

CHAPTER 10

•

IMPLEMENTING CHANGE:
INDUCTION STRATEGIES,
RESISTANCE AND MOTIVATION

While the conditions governing the successful achievement of total quality have been explained, the method of implementing the change has not yet been discussed in concrete terms.

10.1 START-UP, OR HOW TO PRIME THE PUMP

10.1.1 'Up with the Crisis!'

All revolutions originate in a crisis; an unacceptable gap between the current and the desired situation. The perception of this gap and the need for change often occurs too late, since the human mind has great difficulty in modifying its view of a given situation. Well entrenched in our habits and beliefs, we are more inclined to seek confirmation and reinforcement of existing preconceived ideas than to change them. There is a tendency to neglect or ignore negative instances, errors or harbingers of change, and deliberately disconnect the alarm systems. It usually takes a substantial accumulation of proof before we are prepared to modify our current patterns of thought. One of the characteristics of social, cultural or scientific reforms or revolutions is that finally, in the face of all the accumulated evidence, the existing and generally accepted set of assumptions is brutally swept aside, allowing the new model or paradigm to emerge. Thus, for example, it is sometimes not until customers revolt or migrate in droves to the competition, that a corporation will finally consider reviewing its practices. The situation has suddenly become urgent, critical, vital, a crisis has blown up. But long live the crisis! Properly exploited, it can deliver a healthy shock that is able to dismantle vested interests and destabilize complacency, in other words, it can unfreeze the organization and allow change to diffuse throughout and impose a new order.

Occasionally, though this is rare, awareness can help anticipate the crisis. This can happen where management is imbued with a long-term strategic vision. However, the enlightened managers will then have to convince the other senior executives that there is a problem, and in the absence of any dramatic event or beneficial shock to create a burning need to change, this can be a time-consuming process. The positive aspect of such cases is that the corporation then has more resources and time available, giving the management the ability to exercise greater control over the rate of evolution.

10.1.2   Priming the Pump with Quality Circles

From arguments developed in preceding chapters, it should now be clear that the movement must begin at the top. Each head of department or sector should take up his responsibility for quality and make the decision to apply the new model and improvement process. Any attempt that starts at the lowest operation level, with quality circles for example, without adequate awareness and top-down pressure is doomed to failure. It is an easy way to jeopardize total quality and to lose two whole years – the time it will take to realize the error or wait until the rest of the corporation has caught up. Quality circles, though an important factor in the overall approach when implemented at a later, appropriate stage, are certainly not the optimum way of launching the quality movement.

The issue is less clear cut when dealing with services, as the 'front line' is in direct contact with the customer. Quality circles might, therefore, act as direct spokesmen for customers' needs. However, circumspection is recommended since the rest of the organization, particularly the back office and the supporting services, have to be able to cope with the innumerable requests and hopes raised at front line level.

10.1.3   Priming the Pump with a Committed Management Team

Management will only be ready to lead the way if it has tested the model and is convinced of its validity. To ensure this, key executives should be actively involved in the preparation of initial training and the first trial experiments. They could also participate in essential improvement projects and, based on this experience, launch the total quality process with full commitment.

10.1.4   Priming the Pump in a Climate of Trust and of 'Glasnost'

It takes a certain amount of trust and encouragement to be willing to expose problems or errors, to agree to experiment, to take risks, change old habits, or modify one's territory and interactions. In the absence of such a climate, or if the organization is just about to embark upon a major 'rationalization' with lay-offs, there will clearly be few volunteers to join the movement.

10.1.5   Priming the Pump with an Awareness Campaign

Every conceivable method of communication can be used to sell the new model to the entire corporation, and this subject has already been treated at some length.

Many corporations have embarked on one-day to three-day seminars to heighten awareness at all levels of management. The purpose of this exercise is to provide a common language and to reach quickly a critical mass of employees who, if not completely convinced, are at least prepared to look favourably on the initial experiments.

This standard training may be systematic and massive, covering all executives and employees from top to bottom. While this approach is frequently recommended by outside consultants, it does have certain drawbacks.

Firstly, training needs and concerns vary considerably from one department to another, while the method proposed by consultants is often rather standard (conscientious lecturers with thick and detailed supporting files). We would recommend devoting only a half to one full day to the main concepts and methods, and then moving on as quickly as possible to practice and action learning projects in the field. Practising quality in a service, in direct contact with customers, differs substantially from controlling quality in a sophisticated industrial process, while planning quality in a design department is different again.

Secondly, mass training may create a healthy shock if the organization is prepared to benefit from it rapidly, and if the necessary mechanisms to convert tries into results are ready. A hammer blow on the head to wake you up is all very well, but it should go together with organizational change, education and practice.

Another drawback is that an insufficiently action-orientated training programme is liable to lose much of its impact. What will remain six months later if learning has not been materialized and memorized by practice? In any event, whether an awareness seminar is carried out on a corporate-wide scale or not, it is important to use company executives themselves rather than outside consultants. To play their leadership role, managers should absorb and then spread the message, thus reinforcing the credibility of the process.

Another approach, particularly when sufficient time is available, is to develop awareness as experience is gained and illustrative cases become available. This involves selecting a few, very different sectors that are ready to embark upon the venture. For example, a specially threatened sector, or a department led by an enthusiastic manager, or an area already quite experienced, etc. Each sector then chooses a few illustrative projects that will be conducted thoroughly, and then serve as a learning base and case example.

10.1.6 Priming the Pump with Champions and Pilot Experiments, Setting up of a Steering Committee

Whether awareness is massive or opportunistic (diffusing more slowly along the lines of least resistance), it is essential to have demonstration examples and experiments rapidly available to serve as 'locomotive' or 'bellwether' projects. These initial projects will be very carefully watched by the rest of the organization, and if successful will endow the movement with a certain amount of credibility and establish a bridgehead. The choice of these projects should be the responsibility of a small group of determined senior executives who will then champion them. These executives will form the core of the future steering committee responsible for guiding the change process.

Choosing the right executives is essential. Selection for this function should be a promotion for recognized leaders and not a dead-end job for unemployable directors. The future steering committee should contain key upper managers of the departments or divisions concerned. This first core, responsible for setting up initial training, defining the earliest goals and appointing the first project teams, should be empowered to distribute resources and protect ongoing experiments.

What criteria should govern the choice of projects? 'Locomotive' projects should be significant but not so vast they cannot be completed within a limited period of a few months with a high probability of success. The main investment should be time and not technological innovation. The first objective is to show that it is possible to put existing resources to better use and improve the process without spending too much. The greater the number of departments involved and subsequently the more cross-functional the projects, the more convincing the results will be.

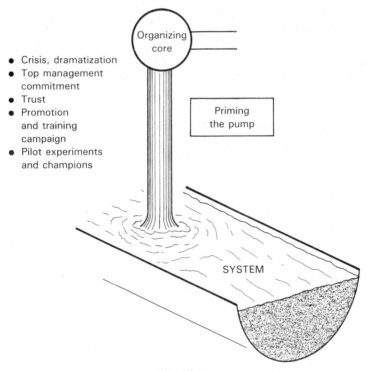

Fig. 10.1

10.2   SPREADING THE MOVEMENT, OR HOW TO MULTIPLY PROJECTS

10.2.1   How Many Projects?

The two stages of the total quality approach, first the elimination of non-conformities and non-useful added values, then the realignment of the system with the customers' needs and wants, have already been described. The final outcome is clearly an improved market position and increased profits, but these results can only be achieved by a vast multiplication of projects and efforts, and numerous improvement, prevention or *ad hoc* teams. Quality may be 1 per cent inspiration, but what counts is the 99 per cent perspiration.

A simple calculation will provide an order of magnitude. Let us suppose that the corporation concerned has an annual revenue of 100 million dollars, and that the cost of poor quality is 20 per cent of that revenue, or 20 million dollars. If our objective is to divide this cost by two over five years, we need to save 2 million dollars per year. If each project can bring in an average of 10 000 dollars, then 200 new projects must be undertaken every year to reach this goal. Similar calculations can be made for every other dimension of progress.

10.2.2   Non-conformity and Non-added-value Reduction Projects

First and Foremost Reduction of Non-conformities

To diagnose worthwhile areas or 'deposits' to work on, physical and visible indicators are vital. Experience has shown that the first areas spotted are usually in the manufacturing or the delivery processes, for the simple reason that measurement of results and parameters is easiest there. Non-conformities, waste or errors can be classified and counted to define the most valuable areas, and then these cut up by successive cross-division into slices small enough to become improvement projects tackled by improvement teams. Projects may be either local or cross-departmental.

Improvement of Global Performance

Inasmuch as they are inextricably linked to other performance indicators such as delivery or flexibility, non-conformity indicators should not be the sole concern of progress teams. The search for viable projects should gradually extend to cover global performance and total 'intelligence' of the process, and soon comprise all non-added-values during transformation: inventory, material handling, transportation, delays, set-up times, breakdowns.

Quality Control in Daily Work

Successful control and stabilization of daily work call for clear specifications, standards and operating procedures. These represent the memory bank of current know-how as practised, taught and updated by the line personnel. Capability analyses, statistical process control and other similar methods may gradually be implemented and extended, project after project.

Moreover, once an improvement has been recorded, it is essential to hold the gain. Here again, the change should be memorized in updated standards and procedures or through the introduction of alarms or foolproofing devices and automation.

Going Upstream

The principle of prevention will lead naturally to a gradual move of projects upstream. As processes are simplified, improved, optimized, disturbances prevented, etc., the total performance will be better controlled. Subsequently, the investment in quality improvement will move from operations and production to engineering and design. As a result, quality is built into the product and the process from the start. A graph frequently quoted by Japanese consultants, similar to the one in Figure 10.2, clearly reflects this evolution.

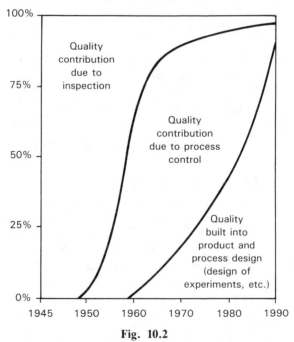

Fig. 10.2

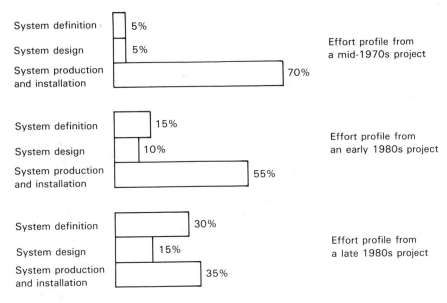

Project management effort remains constant at 20%

Adapted from Martyn A. Ould, *Strategies for Software Engineering* (Wiley, 1990), pp. 162 and 163.

Fig. 10.3

According to Martyn Ould the trend in software development is towards a greater concentration on the definition and design phases. (See Figure 10.3.)

Quality Circles at Last

The gradual top-down spreading of projects will finally reach the bottom line, signalling that the time has come to consider introducing quality circles. Table 10.1 provides a summary of the generally accepted differences between quality circles and quality improvement teams.

The improvement teams may be assisted by facilitators. As the name indicates, a facilitator is a resource placed at the disposal of the group to help it understand the new concepts and methods and to facilitate the co-ordination and implementation of the project. However, facilitators are not supposed to replace the established chain of command, and the natural leader of the improvement group should be the hierarchical boss. When the project is interdepartmental, managers should give a clear 'charter' or mission to guide the team.

Spreading to Services and Support

One by one, the different staff departments and services supporting line operations are gradually affected by the change: data-processing, administration, procurement,

Table 10.1

Characteristics	Quality circle	Quality improvement team
	Comparison Quality circle/Quality improvement	
Project scope	Single department	One or many departments
Project goal	One of a number of minor problems	One of the vital few problems
Origin of participants	One department	One or many departments
Participation basis	Voluntary	Mandatory
Continuity	Unchanged throughout numerous projects	Team dissolved after project completion
Primary mission	Improve human relations and team work	Improve quality and productivity
Secondary mission	Improve quality	Participation

human resources, etc. Not only must these services improve their internal processes, they must also place greater emphasis on cross-functional processes and interdepartmental customer–supplier relations (order taking, invoicing, hiring, etc.).

The more interactive and service-orientated a department becomes, the more difficult it is to measure progress. However, by now the organization should have had enough time to refine its measurement methods to deal with this.

A Multitude of 'Clearing' Projects

Figure 10.4 summarizes the field open to the clearing and extraction of minuses and non-added-values. If we stick to the pump and river analogy, deposits of boulders, stones and gravel represent real or potential problems.

10.2.3 Projects Creating a Competitive Advantage

After spending two or three years clearing up their 'square' or their 'river' and eliminating minuses and non-added-values, managers often discover that quality has become a strategic weapon that can provide opportunities for competitive advantage. The deployment of the customer's voice through the system can highlight significant linkages between departments that are capable of generating 'pluses'.

The river should now be flowing regularly and gently with, here and there, an opportunity for differentiation. (See Figure 10.5.) We have already given numerous examples of linkage opportunities.

10.2.4 Role of the Steering Committee

The core steering committee that was set up to prime the pump and champion the first projects should now be enlarged to keep up with the new projects undertaken. As already explained, this committee plays an essential role in controlling the diffusion of the movement, and hence in defining quality policies, setting goals, appointing, supporting and co-ordinating project teams, planning communication, promotion, training, recognition of merit and holding celebrations.

There is no single 'right' way to go about this. According to their history, their strategy and the level of standardization of their products, their culture and human resources, some firms will place greater emphasis on simplification, error-free processes and value analysis, while others will go all out for just-in-time and stockless production. Some will swear by customer–supplier relations and cross-departmental process analysis, while others will invest massively in automation. Each organization will do well to develop its own specific approach.

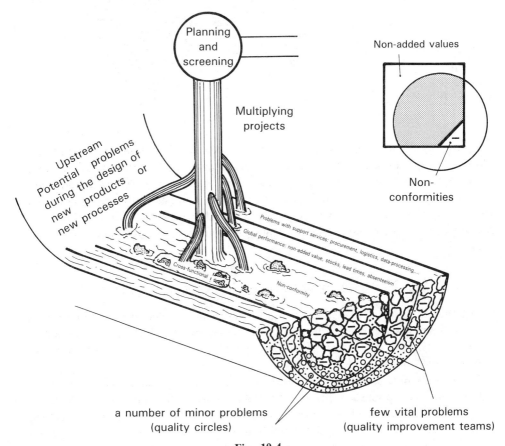

Fig. 10.4

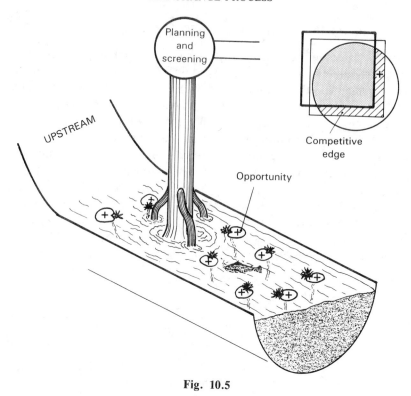

Fig. 10.5

If the organization is fairly large, more than one steering committee should be formed. These could be established at various company levels (corporate, divisions, departments, functions), their membership perhaps comprising the upper managers of each particular area. It should be noted that, as the quality movement develops, the improvement goals set by the steering committee become integrated into the company management system, so that quality improvement becomes part of normal operations.

10.3 CONSOLIDATION, OR CONVERTING TRIES

Once the pump has been primed the movement begins to disseminate throughout the organization in line with the steering committee's strategy and policies. However, to keep up the momentum, the 'tries' must be converted into effective results. (See Figure 10.6.)

The conditions necessary to achieve successful performance and consolidate results can be condensed into the formula shown in Figure 10.7. Successful performance results mainly from the multiplication of these four essential factors; if any one of them is nil, the entire performance will collapse. However, one factor may compensate for another. For example, if objectives are vague and the situation

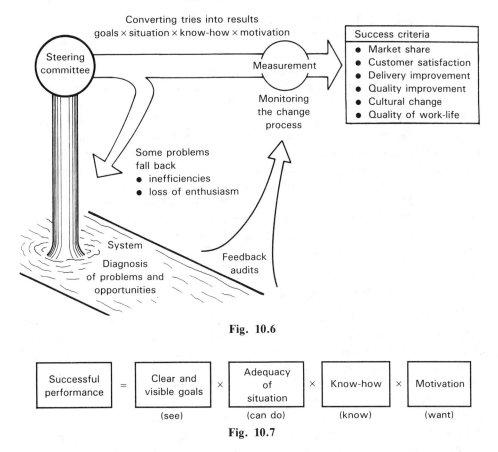

Fig. 10.6

Fig. 10.7

not particularly favourable, motivation is called for to achieve acceptable performance. Let us examine the four factors one by one:

10.3.1 Clearly Stated and Measurable Goals

We have already dwelt at some length on the importance of defining clear, measurable goals and specific, well-defined projects. There are, however, two distinct ways of formulating objectives.

Detailed Centralized Planning

This planning approach, centralized and top down, breaks the final goals down into sub-objectives, sub-sub-objectives, etc., right down to elementary tasks, and then assigns to everyone a precise result they must achieve. However, once they have attained this result, there is no reason for them to do any better. This is one of the major drawbacks of management by objectives.

Moreover, while it is true that management by objectives is inevitable inasmuch as some breakdown of goals is necessary, this method becomes cumbersome when the division is too fine. The breakdown, expressed in directions and goals, should remain general enough to meet grassroots proposals, initiatives and projects. The eternal mirage of the planner has always been to conduct an exhaustive survey of the situation, as if it was possible to carry out a detailed enumeration of all the opportunities or problems present in the process flows. To use the river analogy once more, the ambition is to locate every deposit obstructing the river flow. The more pragmatic solution would be to lower the surface of the water gradually, note the visible turbulences and solve the problems that appear, then continue to lower the level in a rhythm of continuous improvement, project by project.

It is over-ambitious and often illusory to try and penetrate to any undue depth in an attempt to obtain a total picture, a complete and detailed plan, before authorizing action. Even if this was possible, inevitably the situation would have changed in the meantime.

Pulling the Right Strings and Obtaining Visibility

Another approach consists of simply designing the main goals and directions and diagnosing the turbulent areas to start with, and then giving the chosen team sufficient autonomy to make proposals from their own fieldwork. These collected proposals, once aggregated, should match the goals and directions defined by management. Each line of action should be like a rope which can be pulled and tightened to reveal areas for improvement, in the same way as the level of the river can be drawn and lowered in order to display obstacles, problems or opportunities one by one. Instead of freezing the situation into a detailed plan, pulling on these lines of action can highlight the physical difficulties, opportunities and action. Through this visible management, pressure can be exerted on the process itself, rather than on the end result. (See Figure 10.8.)

A number of ropes that have already proved their value can be pulled on: tightening conformance and variance, tightening development and production cycles, tightening flows by reducing inventories, set-up times and breakdowns, streamlining procedures and reducing paperflow, drawing tight manpower, etc.

The danger here is over-ambition, tying to bite off a bigger problem than can be chewed at one time. Rather than trying to swallow a mammoth in one go, the learning and the results are much more effective if the animal is cut up into slices small enough to be digested by improvement teams on the field. (See. Figure 10.9.)

This is a pragmatic way of working physically on the system. To take an expression coined by H. Simon, this approach prioritizes the problems emerging from the 'garbage can', the essential concern being to designate which garbage cans to work on, and what the emergence level should be.

An excellent example of this is quoted in *Moment of Truth* by Carlzon, Chief Executive Officer of Scandinavian Airline Systems: 'We established the general target of having the luggage roll onto the conveyor belt when the passengers arrive at the baggage claim.' Presuming that the current waiting time is fairly long, say twenty minutes, this is an ambitious objective. However, it can be reached, if taken step by step. The first step may aim to reduce the waiting time to fifteen minutes in a month's time. The tightening of the luggage flow during that time will highlight obstacles and delays so that corresponding remedial actions may be taken. Once this objective has been reached two months in a row, it can then be reduced by 20 per cent so that the new goal becomes twelve minutes and so on. Not only is this objective dynamic, it also has an integrating effect by regrouping initiatives and actions as they appear by fieldwork on the system. Once this 'deposit' has been sufficiently exploited, another area can be tackled.

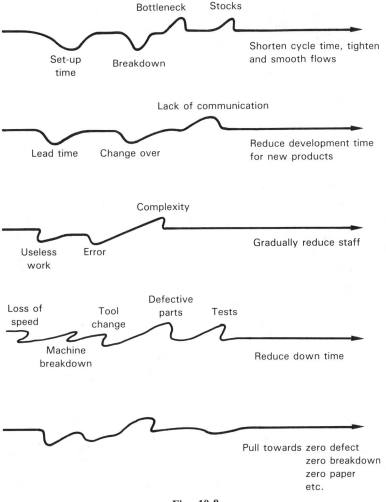

Fig. 10.8

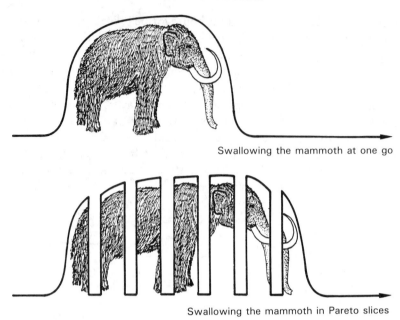

Swallowing the mammoth at one go

Swallowing the mammoth in Pareto slices

Fig. 10.9

A Two-pronged Movement

The two approaches, top down and bottom up, are not incompatible and can be reconciled by successive swings of the pendulum: top-down centralization and strategic definitions of lines of action and priorities, followed by decentralization to free bottom-up initiatives, and so on.

This same movement is found in production planning. While the master production plan defines final overall production within a weekly or monthly time definition, the detailed scheduling of components can be based on a pragmatic, Kanban-type approach, where components are called for only when needed. In this way the overall flow is pushed by the plan, whereas the downstream requirements are pulled by the final customer.

10.3.2 Adequacy of Situation: 'Room to Grow'

Just as athletes are naturally motivated to run in the fastest time, or musicians to perform perfectly, workers would prefer to get a product right the first time, and make something that their customers will approve of. Why don't they always succeed? The reason may be found in the inadequacy of their situation, or because the operation is too difficult or perhaps because their motivation does not match the organizational demands. Hertzberg used to say: 'I want to play the piano, I know how to play the piano ... but I don't have a piano to play on!' The situation is adequate when you have the opportunity to do things, when it is possible for you to act and take initiatives, when you own the problem, when management reduces hassles, controls and constraints.

Managers must not only comprehend the technical system but must also be responsible for changing the organizational set-up. An organizational diagnosis should supplement a technical audit. An analysis of the strategies of various actors and of the organizational structure can aid an understanding of the situation, so that freedom of action while doing the job and an increased level of co-operation between departments can be developed. Clearly, however, as tries are converted into meaningful results, changes of territory, roles and power will occur in at least three domains. We will look at these in turn.

Changing Role of Experts

To an ever increasing extent, the role of experts, of design or method engineers, of maintenance teams, etc., is to organize the processes for which they are responsible on a preventive basis, so that the manufacturer or service deliverer can operate easily and carry out the task right first time. The experts then have to support and supply their internal customers on the shopfloor, or in the front line. Inevitably, they must return to the field to gather information from these customers, information necessary for their preventive work. Line managers are then freer to challenge these experts.

This is a complete turnaround compared with the old, conventional situation, where experts came to lay down the law and play the rescuers and fire fighters (that is when they did not happen to be the fire raisers!).

Enlargement of Operators' Sphere of Action

Process control, as we have seen, requires either greater autonomy and responsibility from operators exercising 'self' control, or foolproofing and automation. To be truly responsible, however, operators should be in a position to measure, correct and improve their own job.

Managers and experts should therefore reorganize work on this basis, for example by focusing and streamlining process flows, or creating independent production cells where operators have scheduling, quality and maintenance responsibilities. This will allow operators to become multiskilled and manage most of the information themselves. Less information being sent upwards means less hierarchy, less bureaucracy and less red-tape. Managers, on the other hand, must be sufficiently knowledgeable about their processes to be able to identify the key variables that must be monitored and the weak points requiring special attention. They will practise management control by exception.

Breaking Down Barriers. Cross-functional or Interdepartmental Co-operation

The customer requirements and demands pulling processes from downstream will lead to the re-establishment of cross-departmental co-operation and customer–supplier relations, a subject already dealt with at some length.

10.3.3   Resistance to Change

Why is there Resistance to Change?

The total quality change process, as previously explained, cannot succeed without a major restructuring of the organization to permit the multiplication of functional and cross-functional teams, and the implementation of the proposed solutions. These changes will lead to new games, new behaviours and new values being established. With adequacy of situation, for example, teams will have some freedom of action to prevent, control or improve. And as the multiplication of experiments brings about new dynamics of technical and sociological change, some resistance may appear in their wake.

The technical and organizational changes may possibly generate resistance to change because they lead to some erosion or loss of power, influence, prestige, authority, technical expertise (ignorance of a new technology or a new skill), information control, territory, job security, etc. As Edgar Schein (1988, p. 295) explains, technical change is less threatening than cultural change: 'A key both to unfreezing and managing change is to create enough psychological safety to permit group members to bear the anxieties that come with examining and changing part of their culture.'

How Can Resistance to Change be Reduced

What follows is a list of several tried and trusted methods:

Creating a Climate of Trust
Threats to tenure, territory or power can paralyze change. By guaranteeing security of employment, by accepting the exposure of problems, by showing commitment and consistency, by getting positive results, etc., in all these ways the company can establish a propitious climate of trust.

Encouraging Participation
The new technical solution or the role change will be more readily accepted if those involved are active participants from the outset, and are in a position to understand and influence the outcome. Moreover, people are generally more convinced by solutions derived from the 'law of the situation', when they are confronted with real constraints and demands, than by solutions imposed from above. Similarly,

'pseudo-participation', which consists merely of selling a pre-determined solution, is generally ineffective.

Providing Enough Time
New behaviours and values take time to become established. In the long run, they will result from the multiplication of experiments and the repetition of new practices. In some cases, a sociological diagnosis may facilitate the establishment of a suitable strategy while in others, the situation will only be unfrozen by the departure of certain managers.

Whatever the case, a biological rhythm should be respected. As Juan aptly expresses it, 'the incubation period for a chicken is twenty-one days. If you heat up the process, you get a boiled egg!'

Negotiating
Clearly then, it is not always possible to proceed as fast as you would like to, or to have the project accepted in one fell swoop. You must analyze what is at stake for each actor, and negotiate compensations, modifications or additional resources; it is important to understand what is vital and what is less so, and to accept compromises. It goes without saying that a certain number of experts and middle managers will see improvement teams as parasitic coalitions, and will secrete powerful antibodies to avoid risky challenges or neutralize anything they perceive as a loss of power.

10.3.4 Know-how and Capability

Once more, we are back to our train of thought concerning the importance of personnel recruitment, promotion and training. The new culture is a technical one, for professionals only.

Technical and technological transfer through outside training, or via external consultants called in to develop and refine the suitable methods, is certainly beneficial, but the development, maintenance, updating and diffusion of relevant know-how and learning should be taken over by managers and employees themselves.

A corporation can only attain strategic supremacy by reinforcing its own professionalism. It is obvious, though, that personnel professionalism and ability go hand in hand with systems capability.

10.3.5 Motivation

For numerous managers, motivation is a miraculous remedy for better performance and results. But what is the evil that this remedy is supposed to cure? Fuzzy and short-sighted objectives, stalemates and top-heavy bureaucracy, on-the-job training ... Motivation can indeed make up for a weakness in the conditions described above and in Figure 10.6. But why not deal with the system first, and improve the objectives, the adequacy of the situation and the know-how before spending more resources on personnel motivation? And incidentally, it should be remembered that motivated people are not always that easy to manage! This being said, two aspects of motivation should be distinguished, as described by Hertzberg (1967).

Getting People to Move

If you treat people well, if you avoid pain, dissatisfaction and bad working conditions, you get people to move and achieve normal performance in their job.

Rewards and bonuses can achieve extra movement but, once given, they are taken for granted. The carrot may get the donkey on his feet, but it is his master that is motivated to proceed.

Conversely, poor working conditions, red tape, hassles or bonus reduction are perceived negatively and lead to definite dissatisfaction. In Figure 10.10, the normal work situation is represented by a square (once again this invaluable symbol). A full square means that, in the absence of dissatisfaction, performance is normal, standard. 'Minuses' in the corner represent dissatisfaction: what makes people unhappy is their work situation and poor 'hygiene' factors. The absence of minuses corresponds to absence of dissatisfaction but is still not true motivation.

Real Motivation

Motivation, by contrast, results from individual freedom of action. People are motivated by what they do, and the more they can do, the more they are motivated. Hence motivation results from the opportunity to act, learn and improve, to achieve a significant return and obtain recognition for one's actions. (See Figure 10.11.) A 'plus' of motivation only appears if people have something meaningful to do. As Hertzberg says, 'If a worker is doing an idiot's work, then

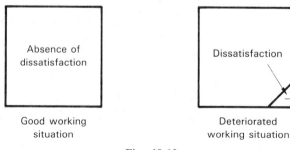

Fig. 10.10

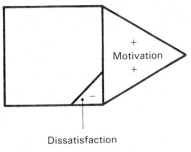

Fig. 10.11

you cannot hold him responsible for cheating at it ... You cannot hold anybody responsible for being an idiot!'

Motivated people have an autonomous motor that sets them in motion from within, and is not started up by the external situation or hygiene factors. But what are these factors of motivation? What is the motivation equation?

A Motivation Equation

A lengthy discourse on the subject of motivation has no place here, so we are offering instead a synthetic image condensed into a formula (based on Hackman and Oldham, 1980). In this formula, shown in Figure 10.12, the essential factors are multiplied to reflect compensation and substitution between them. The factors are explained as follows:

- Task significance – the task is not stupid or trivial. It is meaningful in relation to the rest and allows learning, development, differentiation to take place.
- Task variety – job enlargement and enrichment allow a better use of abilities and lead to multiskill and team work.
- Task identity – the task is complete, identifiable, not piecemeal. It can then be more readily comprehended, owned and improved.
- Autonomy – this is the ability to use one's initiative, to experiment, interact with others, use one's brain and know-how, be responsible and control one's own actions.
- Job feedback – you are less dependent upon someone else telling you what to do. You receive direct feedback from your action, and the faster it occurs the more effective you are. This factor encompasses recognition of efforts and results and celebration of success, as described earlier.

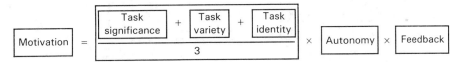

Fig. 10.12

It is clear from this that motivation cannot exist independently of the adequacy of situation, which was the second condition for successful performance (see Figure 10.7). Motivation must, therefore, be built into the production processes very early on, at the design stage when jobs and activities are divided, focused and decentralized.

A final point to be made is that rewards and recognition should not be treated independently of the sociological aspects of co-operation and power games.

10.3.6 Steering Committee Strategies

Although launching the total quality movement is not difficult, developing and consolidating does present more of a problem. This cultural change process postulates constancy of purpose, and can only be established through regular practice and the multiplication of projects and actions. Results only appear after a few years of investment and effort, a serious investment even if the return is considerable.

If we refer back to the cost of poor quality concept, then, as Figure 10.13 shows, the transition from situation I to situation II demands a serious investment in prevention, accentuated here by the curved line. To be free in the long term, quality requires investment in time and training for experimentation, learning or reorganization.

Major Directions

The steering committee's first mission should be to provide orientations and goals, and point out areas needing improvement or with the potential to give a competitive advantage. As already noted, this quality improvement and planning should gradually be integrated into the strategic planning and management system of the organization. These goals and directions will then be adjusted according to the results obtained.

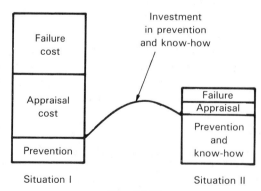

Fig. 10.13

Monitoring the Change Process

The steering committee should monitor the change process as it develops by setting up, on the one hand, 'physical' internal indicators showing specific effort, and, on the other, results obtained (number of projects, training, regular surveys and audits, etc., see Figure 10.14). Indicators measuring specific effort are:

- the number of different sorts of projects (value analysis, conformance, FMEA groups, cross-functional groups, quality circles, etc.)
- the number of projects which are active, pending, abandoned, implemented, certified
- time and money invested
- training budget
- number of staff trained in a given method or discipline
- personnel acceptance of change and motivation
- communication budget and efforts
- number of project presentations
- type and number of awards distributed.

Result indicators are:

- customer satisfaction
- market position
- cost reduction and savings

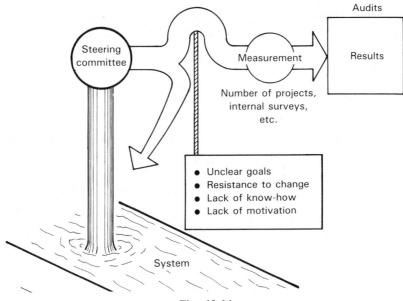

Fig. 10.14

Table 10.2

Categories	Number of points	Percentage
Malcom Baldrige National Quality Award Application Guidelines 1989, second edition, National Institute of Standards and Technology		
1. Leadership and management system	120	12
2. Information and analysis of data and facts	60	6
3. Strategic quality planning	80	8
4. Human resource utilization 　Management 　Employee involvement 　Quality education and training 　Employee recognition 　Quality of worklife	150	15
5. Quality assurance 　Introduction of new products 　Process control 　Measurements and standards 　Audits 　Documentation 　Quality assurance, internal and external	140	14
6. Quality results 　Quality of products and services 　Quality improvement	150	15
7. Customer satisfaction 　Knowledge of customer requirements and 　expectations 　Customer relationship management 　Customer satisfaction methods of 　measurement and results	300	30

Note: Categories considered for the examination of the Malcolm Baldrige US National Quality Award

- lead time reduction for new product development
- cultural change (new values, new behaviours)
- learning and professionalism.

Clearly, a picture of the situation can only be obtained by regular field data collection, reports and audits.

Some companies have taken the opportunity of a challenge, such as the Deming Prize in Japan or the Malcom Baldrige US national quality awards,[*] to mobilize the entire organization and assess regularly where they stand according to the examination categories (see Table 10.2). Major industrial groups, such as Ford, Rank Xerox, Renault have developed a certification examination (supported by visits and counselling) for their suppliers, which also provides an excellent frame of

---

[*] Congress enacted in 1987 the National Quality Awards Law, creating the Malcom Baldrige Awards to be given each year to two companies in manufacturing, services and small business.

reference. (International standards such as ISO 9000 series could be used as well, even though their scope is more limited, as was explained in Chapter 5.)

Managerial System

The steering committee may use the support of a 'bureau' to co-ordinate different actions: screening important projects and appointing teams, training, promotion, communication (creation of a database containing the description of active or certified projects), rewards and recognition, project presentations, celebrations, etc.

Quality Policies

The implementation strategy followed by the steering committee should remain contingent and will depend on the industry, the maturity of the product line, the time pressure or the prevailing culture and the human resources. A sociological diagnosis of the organization, mapping co-operations inter and intra departments and bringing out major uncertainties and sources of discontent, may help the steering committee to move at different speeds on different fronts, the objective being to reach a no-return situation with a critical mass of successful projects as quickly as possible. Alternatively, the committee may define general policies such as:

- quality is the top priority
- merit rating systems should reflect improvements in quality
- scoreboards should be revised to include quality indicators
- upper managers should serve on quality councils or steering committees
- a new product may be put on the market only if, it is better than the product it is replacing (whatever the customer measure), the replaced being either the existing or a competitive product
- participation in improvement groups may be mandatory from shop floor to top management in one type of company while in another, participation may remain on a voluntary basis
- improvement proposals should be implemented as soon as possible.

Finally, it should be stressed that the steering committee is not just another committee covering supporting staff activities, but a body of key executives, determined to get every manager to carry out quality responsibility, and see everyone engaged in the quality process as a way of life.

10.4 MAINTAINING MOMENTUM AND INSTITUTIONALIZATION

This stage is reached once change has been fully accepted. By now, the majority of employees have adopted the new behaviours, and the new values and missions cover total performance. The concern for quality has been integrated at all management levels and naturally at the design and creation stages of new products. As a result, the decisive factor becomes the rate of quality improvement.

Now that quality reform has become part of the landscape and is institutionalized and integrated into the managerial system, the steering committee will naturally melt away into the existing structures.

Ever alert to the customer's needs, wants and desires, the founts of progress no longer run the risk of drying up. Quality dynamics have been set in motion.

10.5 TO SUMMARIZE: WHAT ARE THE PITFALLS?

In this section, we would like to pinpoint the obstacles liable to delay or block the movement towards total quality by retracing the stages previously described one by one, and indicating the pitfalls usually encountered. The list does not, however, claim to be exhaustive.

10.5.1 Start-up or How to Prime the Pump?

Inadequate awareness

'Increases in quality mean increases in cost.'
'Our problem is cutting cost, not improving quality.'
'Quality costs, we can't afford better quality.'
'Never mind the quality, feel the width.'
'We aren't doing that badly, we sell everything we produce and there aren't that many complaints.'
'We're quite ready to repair it if the customer complains.'
'It's not all that good quality, but we can let it go for once.'
'That's the way we've always done it.'
'It's not my fault, I'm not responsible, it's because of the raw materials.'
'If X department or Y supplier did their job properly, we could provide a decent quality level.'
'Quality is a front line problem, it's a problem of motivation.'
'Try a poster campaign for the work-force.'

Initially Launched with Quality Circles, the Movement Ran out of Steam after a Year or Two

'We've already tried, but nobody would follow us.'

Lack of Commitment and Leadership from the Top

'People watch your feet, not your lips.'
'It's my boss who needs convincing.'

'Haven't the time, we've got other things to do.'
'We haven't got the resources.'
'We have a quality manager to manage quality.'
'Do it, but don't involve me.'
'It's a bolt-on technical activity for statistical and quality experts.'
'Management has different priorities.'
'Here comes the new fad, the flavour of the month.'
'BOHICA! Bend over, here it comes again.'

Climate of Lack of Trust and Fear of Change

'We'll be the scapegoats all over again.'
'All this glasnost is just too risky.'
'It's just another way of exploiting us.'
'It means lay-offs and reductions in pay at the end of the day.'
'Success is good and failure is bad.'

Inadequate Communication

'It's all right for those that fly to the moon.'
'This statistical jazz is too sophisticated for us'.
'Our process is unique. Our operators are artists in their own way.'

Overly Ambitious Pilot Projects (Too Vast, Too Difficult), Previous Projects Refurbished and Renamed

'It doesn't work, we've already tried it.'
'We can't see the difference between our standard productivity improvement campaigns and total quality.'
'It's just another cost-cutting campaign.'
'We have already been working on this project for two years.'

10.5.2   Spreading the Movement or How to Multiply Projects

Too Few Projects

Disconnected islands of quality improvement projects or start-ups.
Too much training, not enough action. After corporate-wide training, the general opinion is that enough time has been devoted to quality. People accept and absorb the 1 per cent of inspiration readily enough, but do not get down to work on the 99 per cent perspiration.

Correction of Errors and Non-values

Those who most fear sin are those who are the least familiar with it.
Too much time is spent on the measurement-of-results indicator such as cost of quality, instead of getting into the action and controlling or improving process.
An attempt is made to conduct an exhaustive assessment of all problems rather than to take immediate action and discover the problems as they appear.
Projects undertaken are too vast or not worthwhile.
Troubleshooting leads to a reactive approach: 'If it ain't broke don't fix it!'
The programme loses momentum: there are fewer and fewer problems to pump when you stay on your own 'square' and forget about the customer.

Few Cross-functional and Cross-departmental Projects

'Us versus them' syndrome.

Rediscovering the Customer

'What weighs the most, a pound of "pluses" or a pound of "minuses"?' All too frequently we keep adding pluses, advantages, 'bells and whistles', instead of cleaning the delivery process and dealing with minuses and non-conformity.
'This would be a great business, if it weren't for all the damned customers' (Albrecht and Zemke, 1985, p. 5).

The Steering Committee is Not Doing Its Job

The committee is perceived as having little power. For example the appointed leader is unknown, not liked or on the verge of retiring.
The committee is led by the Director of Quality Assurance. The other departments fail to understand his role and refuse to accept his authority.
Not all services involved in the process are represented on the committee.
Lack of constancy of purpose: indecision, wait-and-see attitude, unclear orientations, fuzzy or changeable priorities.
People are only evaluated on financial, cost or productivity criteria.
Political pressure: some committee members take advantage of their position to settle long-standing scores.
Bureaucratic, authoritarian style.
No provision has been made to supply time and resources. Management keeps adding to participants' workload.
Poor choice of projects.
Poor selection of improvement teams and champions.

Implementation of techniques on an *ad hoc* basis without clarifying total quality concepts (techniques as an end in themselves).

10.5.3 Consolidation or Converting Tries

Unclear Goals and Poor Diagnosis

'No one knew that the problem existed.'
'A man with no target does not have to reach it.'

Inadequacy of Situation

'We can't do anything about it because the problem is beyond our control.'
'We have no opportunity to use our abilities.'
'He's doing an idiot's work! Can you hold him responsible for being an idiot?'
'When you are up to your hips in alligators, it is sometimes difficult to remember that you originally came there to drain the swamp.'

Resistance to Change

'Our employees aren't interested in doing a decent job.'
Apart from the three classic risks of:
- failure to obtain participation
- failure to provide enough time
- failure to take full account of the personal strategies of the actors and the power structure when negotiating,

we also find the usual stumbling blocks:
- climate of uncertainty, insecure job tenure, especially for middle managers
- lack of communication: problems are not communicated upwards
- project proposal or implementation delayed by lengthy and discouraging agreement and certification procedures
- refusal to co-operate, to exchange information, etc., in general resistance to power erosion.

'We have met the enemy, the enemy is us.'

Inadequate training or ability

Inadequate hiring procedures.
Required skills seem out of reach.
Insufficient investment in training.
Inadequate technical training.
Training is too theoretical, not action-orientated.
Training is substituted for rules of thumb.

Tools and methods are inappropriate or too general.

The company bought expensive expert packages as an end in itself. After the initial enthusiasm wears off, the method falls into disuse.

Motivation

'Our real problem is people motivation.'

'How can we motivate our employees?'

Systematic recourse to motivation to compensate for lack of planning, organization or training.

Delay in recognition of merit or even forgetting to thank people.

Failure to consider people as the essential resource.

Inadequate Management and Monitoring of the Change Process

Poor planning.

Poor scoreboard

No periodical audits.

CHAPTER 11

•

METHODS AND TOOLS: AN
ORIENTATION MAP

Experience corrects man daily, but this is because he reasons properly and experimentally on the basis of his observations, for otherwise he would never correct himself. (Claude Bernard, 1865)

The continuous improvement process launched by the total quality movement leads inevitably to a technical and experimental culture that pervades the entire organization.

In this environment, progress is based on a clear and systematic methodology, soundly established on experience and facts. Every individual has become both an observer and an experimenter. Claude Bernard, quoted at the beginning of the chapter, was one of several experts in the field of experimental medicine. As he has written,

It is possible to learn, i.e. to acquire experience from our environment, in two ways: empirically and experimentally. Initially there is a sort of subconscious, empirical learning or experience obtained by practising every object ... However, this obscure and spontaneous approach has been elevated by the scientist into a clear and reasoned method.

This explains the importance of factual observation, of measuring and recording, defining symptoms with precision, testing opinions and hypotheses and so on. Consequently, statistics emerge as the ideal language for describing, counting, classifying, analyzing, testing collections of data. Statistics can be an impartial judge, or can provide powerful tools with which to extract relevant information from time series or masses of data.

Again as Claude Bernard has written, 'When facts are in conflict with a prevailing theory, you must accept the facts and abandon the theory even though the theory, supported by great names, is generally recognized.' Sticking to facts and 'speaking with data' mean multiplying field experiments and varying the perspective. Hence the importance of mixed quality teams, and the use of creative approaches like brainstorming or lateral thinking. To quote Claude Bernard one last time: 'When breaking new ground, you should not remain passive because of any false modesty based on the fear of making mistakes. You should not be frightened to express views, however rash, in order to stimulate research in every direction.'

To provide an orientation map of the main tools and methods available, this chapter will be organized according to the following three headings:

1. Statistical language and statistical tools.
2. Overall vision and graphic modelling.
3. Systematic progress methods.

11.1 STATISTICAL LANGUAGE AND STATISTICAL TOOLS

Statistics are a good tool with which to observe and record facts, to manipulate and analyze masses of data, to test hypotheses and improve decision making.

11.1.1 Measurement

Statistics always begin with the measurement and recording of certain characteristics, also called variables, of the original population or series of observations. However, real phenomena, in order to be measured, must be coded according to a more or less arbitrary grid. When the variable of interest is qualitative, observations must be sorted into categories according to a code, a directory or a classification, a list of defects, for example. After distribution into different categories, observations are counted to obtain a frequency or a relative frequency distribution. When the variable is quantitative, direct numerical measurement is possible, but depends on the method and the tool utilized. After distribution into predetermined numerical classes, observations are counted to obtain frequency, relative frequency and cumulated frequency distributions. In both cases, direct observation and measurement in the field is essential.

11.1.2 Simplification of Data

Histograms and Indicators

A frequency distribution or histogram is a simplified representation of the phenomenon under study. The mass of observations has been distributed and allocated into a small number of classes. From the frequency histogram, a more or less artistic curve can be extrapolated, which may resemble a well-known theoretical distribution, such as the normal distribution or the binomial distribution.

Concentration or Pareto Analysis

When the phenomenon or population under study is far from being homogeneous, different sub-groups can be identified on a cumulative distribution. At one end, we may have a small number of observations of vital importance and at the other, a host of observations of minor importance. For example, 10 per cent of the problems may represent 90 per cent of the cost of poor quality, while 90 per cent of the problems represent only 10 per cent. This is variously known as concentration analysis by statisticians, as the Pareto principle by Juran, as the A, B, C distribution when three classes are distinguished, and as the 20-80 rule when only two classes are singled out.

Central Tendency and Dispersion

Simplification may be taken a step further. The mass of data can be reduced to one or two meaningful indicators: a measure of central tendency (average or mean, median, mode) and a measure of dispersion (range, fractiles, variance or standard deviation).

11.1.3 Random Unidimensional Phenomena

Random Phenomena

Random phenomena can be represented by series of observations which are individually unpredictable, i.e. are independent of one another, but remain stable over time, i.e. stationary. It is only under these conditions that the chronological sequence of the series can be disregarded, and the data compacted into a frequency distribution that may resemble a known distribution, which can be normal, binomial or other.

When dealing with a series of observations we must, therefore, first check whether or not it is random. If not, we must extract all specific information and special 'causes' which may have influenced the behaviour of the variable analyzed (shift of the mean, wider variability, etc.).

Traceability

When several production streams are mixed, the resulting batch may appear random. However, by tracing back each stream (the production of an individual machine, for example), it is usually possible to observe less regular series and to identify causes of deviation by correlation between operating parameters and results. This makes it essential to analyze time series or spatial sequences as closely as possible to the original process, before deciding to disregard the chronological or geographical information and treat final batches like memory-less distributions.

Analysis of Time Series

The principle underlying statistical process control (SPC) consists of identifying any 'abnormal' deviation from the expected average or the expected range by taking samples directly from the production process, 'on-line' (see Chapter 4).

For example, a sudden jump of the average diameter of a sample of parts recorded on the control chart when a new production shift takes over may be explained by a special cause: perhaps the two shifts use different measuring tools or follow different procedures. Statistical process control is then, a widely used methodology to spot, on-line, special causes of variation and to stabilize, and later improve, production processes.

Analysis of Spatial Sequences and of Geographical Concentrations

The same principle applies to spatial sequences. In the manufacture of rubber gloves, for example, the concentration of defects around the thumb triggers off an analysis to discover the spatial causes involved.

11.1.4 Multidimensional Statistics

Statistical units or observations can be described by various characteristics or dimensions. Any multidimensional analysis then supposes the transcription of the mass of information available into a rectangular table or matrix, with as many lines as observations, and as many columns as dimensions or variables. If all the variables or columns of the table have identical roles, they are treated by factorial analysis or classification methods. If certain columns play a special role, analysis of variance and regression or segmentation methods are resorted to.

11.1.5 Experimental Plans and the Taguchi Method

Agronomists were the first scientists to use analysis of variance and regression methods to test the influence of certain variables or factors on the final result. In the early 1920s, Fisher suggested organizing and planning experiments by combining several factors instead of studying a single factor at a time. For example, let us suppose that a farmer has to decide which variety of wheat to grow, depending on the nature of the soil, the climatic conditions, etc., in order to get the best possible yields. By varying all factors simultaneously, according to a well-defined plan which uses the smallest possible number of experiments, decisive results can be obtained more economically than by the method of varying only one factor at a time. Not surprisingly, due to its complex theoretical features and the difficulties of calculation, it was many years before this method became widely used in industry.

Meanwhile, towards the end of the 1950s, Genichi Taguchi was working in two directions at once:

— product and process design for more 'robust' function. There is no point in getting excellent performance in the laboratory if small variations in process parameters or in environmental variables cause a loss to the customer or even to society. Can a more stable operating point be found, and can key parameters be better controlled to reduce the loss caused by variability?

— popularization of experimental design. Taguchi developed user friendly designs of experiments and tables, with which the influence of different factors on the final result could be tested simultaneously and efficiently.

Despite criticism of its excessive simplification by certain experts, the Taguchi method has spread rapidly. Thanks in particular to the American Supply Institute of Chicago, originally created by Ford, the automotive industry has played a leading role in its propagation. The method proceeds through eight stages, as follows:

1. Formalizing objectives
2. Searching for factors
3. Selecting the plan of experimentation
4. Conducting the experiments
5. Checking the validity of experiments
6. Analyzing results
7. Confirming solutions found by experiments
8. Drawing up recommendations.

11.1.6   In Conclusion

Statistics is a privileged language for speaking with data, solving with data, proving with data and deciding with data. As the total quality movement spreads throughout the organization, it should be learned and practised by everyone. This explains the considerable effort undertaken to popularize it and also why the simplest tools,[1] such as control charts, histograms or Pareto analysis are so often taught. They are simple enough to be explained to anybody.

11.2   OVERALL VISION AND GRAPHIC MODELLING

To visualize a problem is, for the most part, to solve it. Western education favours systematic analysis and linear reasoning, the logical and mathematical intelligence supposedly located in the left side of the brain. A manager, however, is mainly a person of action and vision, who must cope with a large number of situations simultaneously. This means he must also make use of the right side of his brain, which is more specialized in pattern recognition and global perception. The advantage of a diagram or a graph representation is to condense all the information available into a single picture, enabling comparisons to emerge which would otherwise have remained invisible. Another advantage of visualization is that it encourages group work by facilitating the exchange of views.

There is a long list of tools available. The following mentions only a few:

— flow charts
— interaction diagrams
— layout diagrams
— fishbone diagrams, also known as cause and effect diagrams or Ishikawa
    diagrams
— matrices
— fault trees.

11.3 SYSTEMATIC PROGRESS METHODS

11.3.1 Analysis of Problems and Opportunities

The Scientific Method

There exists a 'scientific', prescriptive method for the analysis and solution of problems which claims to be more effective and economical than our habitual empirical and limited approach. Famous consultants such as Kepner and Tregoe (the rational manager) and Juran (the quality improvement process) have helped to popularize this method, which is nothing more than the good old scientific approach recommended by many and by Claude Bernard in particular.

According to these authors, the method is broken down into five, six or seven stages. We would love to stick to the magic number seven but, for the sake of simplicity and of graphical representation, we have selected a five-stage approach, shown in Figure 11.1. This approach is very close to the six stages in Juran's 'universal breakthrough', shown in Figure 11.2. The US utility company, Florida Power and Light, has instigated a very successful company-wide quality improvement programme, based specifically on a well-structured problem-solving

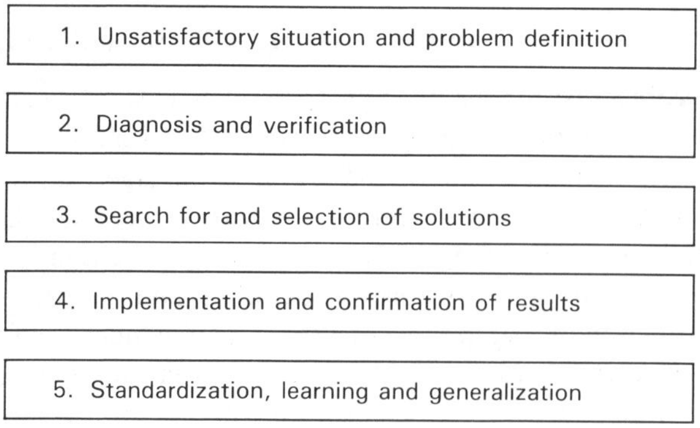

1. Unsatisfactory situation and problem definition

2. Diagnosis and verification

3. Search for and selection of solutions

4. Implementation and confirmation of results

5. Standardization, learning and generalization

Fig. 11.1

1. Proof of the need and project identification

2. Organization to guide the project

3. Diagnosis, organization and breakthrough in knowledge

4. Breakthrough in results and remedial action

5. Breakthrough in cultural resistance to change

6. Control at new level

Fig. 11.2

1. **Theme**: identify a theme and the reason for improvement

2. **Current situation**: select a problem and target for improvement

3. **Analysis and diagnosis**: identify and verify the root cause

4. **Counter-measures**: plan and implement counter-measures

5. **Verification of results**: confirm that the target has been met

6. **Standardization**: prevent the problem and its root causes from recurring

7. **Future plans**: what should be done about remaining problems

Fig. 11.3

methodology in seven stages, inspired mainly by Japanese consultants. This is shown in Figure 11.3.

The three approaches are very similar, but we have adopted a five-stage methodology primarily to fit the graph representation in Figure 11.4. The top part of the 'V' symbol (the first three stages) represents the opening and the creativity necessary to discover as many problems, hypotheses or solutions as possible. This opening is essential when scanning through an unsatisfactory situation and searching out a valid problem. The opening is needed again at the outset of diagnosis to generate as many theories and points of view as possible and finally, some creativity is necessary to provide solutions. The V is turned upside down when

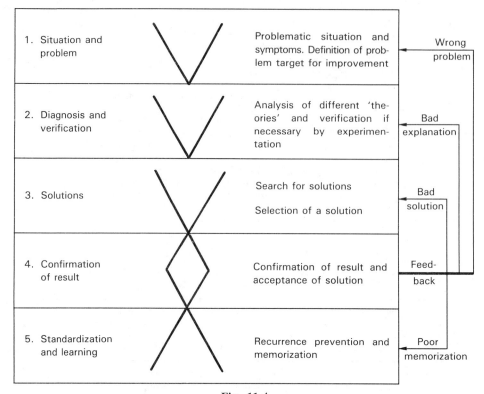

1. Situation and problem		Problematic situation and symptoms. Definition of problem target for improvement	Wrong problem
2. Diagnosis and verification		Analysis of different 'theories' and verification if necessary by experimentation	Bad explanation
3. Solutions		Search for solutions Selection of a solution	Bad solution
4. Confirmation of result		Confirmation of result and acceptance of solution	Feedback
5. Standardization and learning		Recurrence prevention and memorization	Poor memorization

Fig. 11.4

the solution adopted must be generalized to other similar situations, after standardization. The narrow part of the V represents a closure: closure when choosing the problem, closure when eliminating the wrong theories and discovering the main cause, closure when deciding the solution to be implemented. Opening, closing – two meaningful moments that should be clearly separate.

Finally, we should note the specific confirmation phase to check that the problem and its root causes have been decreased, and that the target for improvement has been achieved. Feedback to other phases permits further adjustment.

This problem-solving process may be improved by team work which can provide, amongst other things, creativity and varied points of view. The influence of the organization (steering committee, management, experts) varies with each phase considered. (See Figure 11.5.)

The Empirical Approach

This is all very well in theory, but what about our normal, more empirical approach? When faced with a problem, we tend to react and proceed by trial and error, searching through the repertoires of possible solutions stored in our memory,

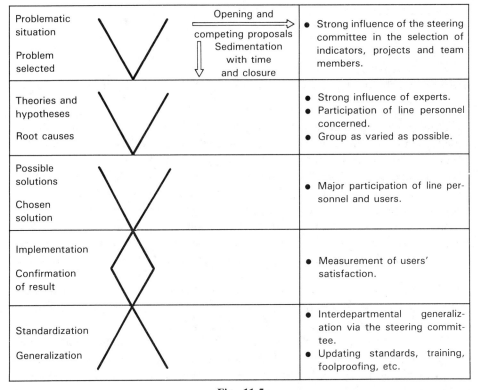

Fig. 11.5

until we find a satisfactory one. We then stop, only too happy to have got rid of all constraints and impossibilities. This approach is triggered by symptoms and stops once a solution (often a palliative solution as the search remains local for most of the time) has been found. Diagnosis then appears as a post-rationalization, as a justification of the choice. We observe a sequence of the type shown in Figure 11.6.

This approach is often called troubleshooting or fire fighting. We can illustrate

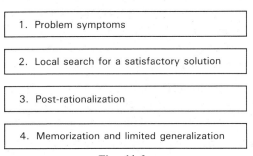

Fig. 11.6

it with a simple example taken from Kaoru Ishikawa:

Problem: A machine is attached to the wall by four bolts. One of the bolts keeps snapping.

Solution: Replace the bolt with a bigger one.

Diagnosis: The bolt snapped because its diameter was not right.

Clearly, we have gone from the symptom to a palliative solution, which can then be generalized by replacing all four bolts. In fact, the root cause of the problem was the vibration of the machine during operation, which means the right solution was to eliminate the spurious vibration. One step was omitted before we rushed into action: the diagnostic phase. To avoid any recurrence and eliminate that vibration permanently we must now change the design or the procedures, etc. Correcting the problem is not the end of the story. Why was the company unable to detect vibrations when the machine prototype was tested and validated? How can we anticipate, prevent problems and generalize our learning? The answer would be to introduce a specific question about potential vibrations at the design stage, when a new prototype is validated or certified.

Finally, we should note an important aspect of trial learning. When a solution which seems to work is found under conditions of stress and emotional involvement (panic, crisis), it will be remembered and repeated indefinitely. 'Once bitten, twice shy.' In such a case, some problematic situations may continue to be avoided without being really explored, because the original trauma remains even though the environment has changed. Such cases are the source of ritual behaviours, superstitions or phobia.

Actors in the Organization

A problem is solved and decisions are made by 'actors' in an organization. When participating in a decision, each individual finds or builds his or her own solution from their own repertoires, from their own perception of the situation and according to their personal strategy.

Every actor sees the problem in the light of his or her own perceptual map, according to the seat or the 'square' they are occupying. This perception varies according to an individual's background, education and profession. When faced with a crisis, an accountant will advise a financial solution, whereas a sales manager will propose a new marketing approach and a production manager will talk in terms of quality control or cost cutting. As Dearborn and Simon (1985, p. 140) explain,

> Presented with a complex stimulus, the subject perceives in it what he is 'ready' to perceive; the more complex or ambiguous the stimulus, the more the perception is determined by what is already 'in' the subject and less by what is in the stimulus.

In addition to this perceptive bias, the personal strategy of actors must also be considered.

In one firm, for example, the maintenance manager's reluctance to introduce preventive maintenance and operator training was explained by his perception of such changes as an unfavourable modification of role and a loss of power. In his view, they meant he would no longer directly control the breakdown or the crisis, but would have to anticipate and plan on the basis of data he would have to obtain from the production operators.

In another example of a firm manufacturing electrical appliances, the solution adopted to overcome the problem of high costs and late deliveries was to put the responsibility on the production manager and fire him at regular intervals. When questioned about the resulting chaos, the production manager could only point his finger (quite rightly) at the design department which, by constantly modifying prototypes and drawings, was to a great extent responsible for the mess. But the design department was too powerful to change its attitude and take the problem upstream.

Thus the perceptive bias of actors and their personal strategies can completely reverse the prescriptive sequence we have just described. The problem is posed in terms of the solutions proposed by the actors. The agenda of problems considered by the organization is derived from the solutions and best interests of the actors in positions of power or authority. As seen by the design department, for instance, the problem is the inability of the production manager to be sufficiently flexible and well organized to adapt his department.

In conclusion, the further we are from a positive problem-solving situation with clear issues, the more important it becomes to pay special attention to the 'political' aspect of the situation and the role of the players involved. The choice of the members of the steering committee and the selection of the improvement team then become even more important than the method used to solve the problem.

The scientific method cannot, therefore, be applied in all situations. However, when sufficient time is provided and there exists a will for clarification, this method does enable us to proceed systematically and go back to facts and experiments, in order to get rid of partial opinions and preconceived ideas. Let us review the different stages of our prescriptive approach in greater detail.

Observation of the Situation – Definition and Selection of the Problem to be Tackled

Measuring and Amplifying the Discrepancy or the Gap

A problem results from a discrepancy, a gap, a dissonance between the expected situation and the perception of an unsatisfactory situation. There is a problem on one side, but an opportunity on the other side if an active search is instigated to surpass expectations. (See Figure 11.7.) Clearly, then, a problem or an opportunity is defined in relation to an expected outcome or a level of aspiration. For example, if my car broke down, I could define the problem with reference to the satisfactory

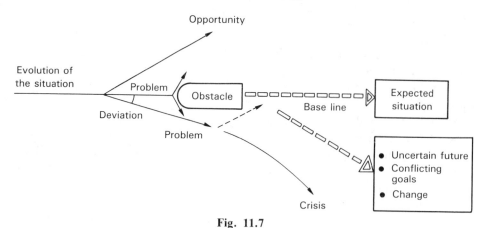

Fig. 11.7

situation, 'I should be on time for my appointment', or with reference to the unsatisfactory situation, 'I'm going to be late'.

If, on the contrary, the situation is defined by an action verb – 'My car has broken down, I must repair it' – the risk is that I may solve the wrong problem; have the car repaired but miss my appointment. Expressing the problem in the form of a solution is often reacting by force of habit or job conditioning. The symptom demands the action, and the action defines the problem.

In order to express the problem it is thus essential, on the one hand, to define the expectations, the references or the standards and, on the other hand, to measure the discrepancies and the symptoms carefully through direct fieldwork.

In fact, our perceptive ability is essentially based on our capacity to detect deviations. The Kepner and Tregoe method, for example, amplifies the deviation by contrasting the difference between what the problem is and what it is not, with a series of questions:

— What is the problem? What is not the problem?
— Where did it happen? Where did it not happen?
— When was it observed? When was it not observed?
— etc.

It is also possible to magnify the deviation by changing the scale (for example, expressing the barely noticeable level of 1 per cent as 10 000 parts per million) or by contrasting and dramatizing the problem.

Let us take as an example Florida Power and Light which supplies electricity to homes and industrial plants. One of the situations to which customers are most sensitive is the reliability of electrical services. Instead of considering a service availability index, an indicator which always looks good, FPL decided to do the opposite. They defined an unavailability index, taking into account not only the duration of the cut-offs but also the number of customers affected. (See Figure 11.8.) In this way FPL was able to set goals, such as: decrease the number

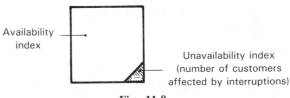

Fig. 11.8

of customer interruptions from 55 000 this year to 40 000 next year. With this indicator, it was also possible to diagnose the most serious causes of interruption for customers and make improvements step by step.

Clear visualization of discrepancies is important because we tend to reinforce whatever confirms our established perception of a situation, and to discard whatever invalidates or disturbs it. Perceptual maps are stable. Symptoms or early warning signals too often tend to be neglected.

Formulating the Right Problem

As already stated, a problem appears as a discrepancy between the actual situation and the reference line (standard, goal, level of expectation). But there are problems that are ignored because that reference does not exist or has been lost (unknown or uncertain), forgotten or is not observed (conflicting goals). It may also be that the reference has not been updated, and is no longer adapted to the new situation.

All too frequently, obvious solutions are not implemented because the problem did not appear to exist. Carlzon quotes a case where the transport of parcels took too long. Following an analysis of the interdepartmental process and the measurement of the transport time, the main bottleneck emerged. The solution was simple: a wall had to be broken down and another loading point installed. Improvement was instantaneous. Why had it not been done before? Because no one had measured the total transport time before.

An essential management responsibility is to identify decisive indicators that will help set the list of areas to be examined and problems to be solved.

Selecting Projects

The 'V' shape or funnel representation of the various stages of the method brings out clearly two essential dimensions: the time dimension and the opening/closing dimension. With time, choices settle down. The selection of projects may be

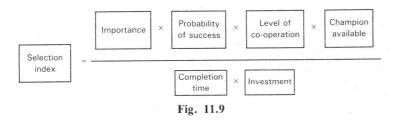

Fig. 11.9

assisted by a multi-criteria formula of the type shown in Figure 11.9. These criteria can be defined as follows:

— importance – what is at stake, visibility, exemplary nature
— probability of success – well-defined project, accessible, good team expertise
— level of co-operation – favourable climate and participation
— champion available – existence of a motivated and well-trained champion
— completion time – a good project should have a deadline and should not last more than a few months
— investment – mainly time and training.

We should note again that the choice of the team is sometimes more important than the choice of the project. It is the team, correctly orientated by its tactical objective, that will be responsible for defining and analyzing the appropriate 'slice' after fieldwork has taken place.

Potential Problem Analysis

Should we wait till we hit a tree before changing direction? It is essential to anticipate problems and prepare preventive solutions. The main difficulty results from the great variety of potential problems to be considered. For this reason the well-known failure mode and effect analysis (FMEA) method classifies potential failure modes and organizes their treatment by order of importance. The classification index is obtained by multiplying three scores from one to ten: a severity score, a probability of occurrence score and a probability of non-detection score. The rest of the FMEA approach is very similar to our problem-solving approach: diagnosis and solution for each failure mode investigated, then confirmation and standardization. The generation of potential failure modes can be systematized by tools such as a fault tree analysis. Many other methods have been developed specifically for reliability and maintenance studies but the same principles apply.

Opportunity Analysis and Value Analysis

Though we do tend to review what seems to be faulty or problematic, we do not often challenge what is acceptable and even less what is good. This is not because a situation has no problem that cannot be improved. We often look for opportunities when it is too late to do so – the crisis is already upon us and there is no time left. Value analysis is an example of a methodology used to challenge what is taken for granted. The method is based on two simple but devastating questions:

— 'Why are you doing that?'
— 'How can you do it more simply and more effectively?'

There is no diagnostic phase. You go directly from opportunities disclosure to the search for solutions and the confirmation of results (see Chapters 5 and 7).

Diagnosis and Verification

This phase, although absolutely essential, is, as we have noted, often missed out. The main reason for this lies not in the technical aspect of the problem, as methods and experts are often readily available, but in the willingness to provide attention, time and resources. During the opening moment, creativity and group work sessions, with the participation of all those involved in the problem, will generate a plethora of hypotheses and theories. The fishbone or cause-effect diagram is very popular at this stage because it is simple and quite visual. The closing moment will consume most energy as it is essential to refute, with facts and experiments if necessary, the maximum number of hypotheses and keep only the most probable causes. Experimental plans, testing several factors simultaneously, are very useful here. (See Chapter 7).

Search and Selection of Solutions

Once again, it is important to distinguish clearly between the opening (generation of solutions) and the closing moment. Selection of the solution may be assisted by a multi-criteria index of the type shown in Figure 11.10. These criteria can be defined as follows:

effectiveness – percentage of problems solved and other problems created
control of implementation – Can the team implement? How many people need to be involved and convinced?
ease of implementation – What are the obstacles, resistances, aids?
investment – costs, resources, time, training.

Implementation and Confirmation of Results

Only concrete field monitoring of results can demonstrate the success of the solution adopted. The problem-solving process is not linear, but iterative. This phase generates feedback to modify and eventually adjust the problem definition, the diagnosis, the solution and the learning.

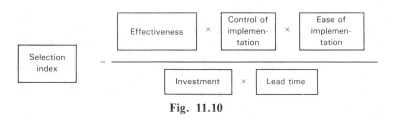

Fig. 11.10

Standardization, Learning and Generalization

Remedial action is not enough. It is essential at this stage to hold the gains, and prevent any recurrence through new standards and operating procedures, training, foolproofing or automation. It is also essential to erase former standards, procedures or know-how which have been superseded, and make sure they are forgotten.

Standards and procedures are part and parcel of daily practice. They should be updated manually when necessary, and not locked away in filing cabinets or the company archives. This explains why the examiners for the Deming Prize often demand to see the working documents and procedures, which must be handed over within three minutes of asking.

Some errors and problems are simply due to the absence of a standard or a non-observance of existing standards. In such cases it is pointless to return to the problem and to diagnose it all over again, you should simply analyze how the know-how is maintained and disseminated. Figure 11.11 shows the questions to be asked.

11.3.2 Tightening Flows

Tightening production flows is a systematic and extremely effective method of making problems visible and improving the process, project by project. Work in

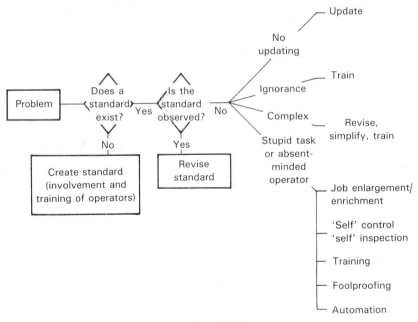

Fig. 11.11

process inventories and storage areas are gradually reduced, production cycles shortened, scrap and machine down-times reduced. Flow tightening improves process visibility and fosters responsibility and co-operation (See Figure 11.12.)

The method goes under various names: flow tightening at Renault; RAC, or replenishment of actual consumption, at Valeo; kanban at Toyota; continuous flow manufacturing at IBM and, more generally, JIT (just-in-time), or stockless production. The principle is the same: flow tightening reveals seams of waste, non-added values and poor quality.

It should be noted, however, that the method only applies to regular flows. Variety of product mix is thus essential to maintain a sufficient level of flexibility. For example, if the process has to produce 400 cars regularly day after day, flexibility and adjustment to demand will be obtained by the variety of the mix, for example, 40 different sorts of car on the same production line.

11.3.3 Total Productive Maintenance or TPM

The goal of this method is to improve the running time of equipment by eliminating the main causes of down-time. Operators participate in the maintenance of the facility and in the preparation of prevention by supplying better information. The

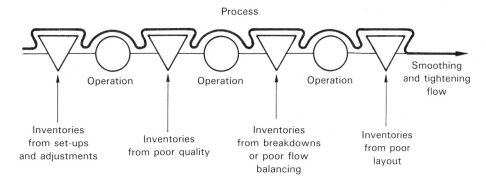

Fig. 11.12

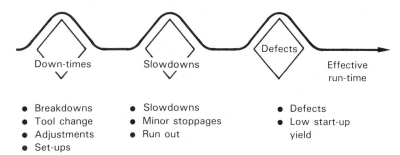

Fig. 11.13

method usually unfolds in five stages:

1. Improvement of a facility, used as a pilot experiment
2. Organization of self-maintenance
3. Organization of programmed preventive maintenance (specialists)
4. Technical training courses
5. Preparation of initial maintenance of new facilities.

The effective run-time is now the indicator, the line that will be pulled on to reveal problems, down-times or disruptions. (See Figure 11.13.)

NOTE

1. The seven magic tools most often referred to are the Pareto analysis, the fishbone diagram, the flow chart, the run chart, the histogram, the correlation graph and the control chart.

CONCLUSION

In the course of this book we have retraced the development of the quality concept, whose extraordinary career finally gave marketing and production the opportunity to meet and merge. As we have seen, quality is first and foremost the customer's perception of an offer produced in conformance with the promise. By allowing the voice of the customer to penetrate every workshop and department, the quality dynamic pursues the impossible task of squaring the customer's circle through gradual adjustment and the quest for that decisive, though always ephemeral, competitive advantage.

As our short history has demonstrated, quality can only be lastingly established through the unflagging accumulation of an organization's know-how, and by the conservation and transmission of its learning. Cultural transformation and professionalization are only attained after several years of daily practice of prevention, control and improvement of the system.

Although the inadequacies of the Taylorian approach (over-specialization, separation of planning from execution, priority given to productivity control by results and costs) have been highlighted, it has not been totally rejected. What we propose is moving beyond this and building quality in from the start, maintaining and improving the processes and the system through a deeper understanding of them. Total quality cannot be compared with a mere cost reduction programme, which often consists of blind overall cuts. These invariably lead to a reduction in quality, as corners are cut off the square of the offer.

Total quality is a systematic method of learning at the level of each process, as well as the level of the whole organization. As people are empowered to act they begin to feel responsible for polishing, improving, simplifying or redeploying their own process. Everyone works intelligently in his or her own sphere, using their brain to make intelligent cuts and exhaust improvement possibilities before automation or major investment is finally necessary.

It is, of course, important to set objectives and to achieve results, but we propose going beyond management by objectives and management by results. Management for quality is a management for objectives. It means changing over from the final inspection of results to stabilization of the process by controlling parameters upstream, and making the results less sensitive to disturbances through the optimization of those same parameters.

Management for quality means striving to understand better the technical and social system for which one is responsible. Managers become more concrete, more physical and, like a sports coach, are not content merely to accumulate championship points. In their new role, they proceed methodically, multiply measurements and identify those essential parameters which are decisive for performance. They analyze weak points, suggest improvements and meanwhile try to develop the technique that will guarantee an undisputed advantage.

Management by results, in contrast, is short-sighted and insufficient. Failure to look beyond results is tantamount to encouraging tinkering and trickery, and often leads only to clan warfare and putting the blame on others. Managing for objectives postulates working on the system, rather than trying to influence the thermometer.

Cultural change will result from the concrete, regular and systematic practice of prevention, control and improvement. This more professional and technical culture leads to increasing delegation, autonomy and ownership. It also brings about greater customer–supplier co-operation, and re-establishes experts in their role of assisting on-line and front line personnel to understand their system better, and solve their own problems. By permeating the entire organization, the quality dynamic helps to combine the ever necessary economies of scale and specialization with economies of co-operation.

The economy of co-operation concept is most useful at the multiple customer–supplier interfaces, between departments or along certain cross-functional processes, such as the introduction of a new product. The voice of the customer must be deployed, and heard loud and clear throughout the workshops and services. This means improving linkages, not only to reduce poor quality, delays or waste, but also to provide better service and create a decisive difference.

However, co-operation does not come naturally. It requires a diagnosis and comprehension of the sociological and relational structures, and an understanding of the roles of the actors. Only then can customer-orientated co-operation be achieved.

We have endeavoured to outline the conditions necessary for the implementation of quality reform: top management commitment, the dramatization and communication of successful pilot experiments to prime the pump, followed by the rapid multiplication of projects based on visible measurements, diagnosis and audits to discover directions to follow and lines to pull. This can only happen in the context of adequate time, training and opportunities.

A steering committee then becomes essential to lead the change process, and monitor the conversion of tries into results. By modifying policies and structures, this committee will help to identify and remove obstacles to the development of know-how and co-operation, thus promoting the development of professionalism and education. The committee should also co-ordinate the recognition and celebration of efforts and successes.

To steer the quality change process itself, the focus should be not only on results, such as a cost of quality reduction or a better market share, but also on the monitoring of efforts throughout the organization by regular technical and social indicators, surveys or audits. Clearly, exerting pressure on every manager to achieve and display short-term results will not further the quality dynamic, which needs time to gather momentum. A manager who changes his job every two years would be unable to apply himself to the task seriously. The quality dynamic results from the multiplication of preventive, control and improvement actions to discipline the system.

But in the quality reformation, do not certain cultures have an advantage, given their natural inclination to respect discipline? This factor probably has some influence, at least in the early stages of the process, but on balance we feel that this discipline can be best acquired through the daily practice of the method described, and that cultural change results from the multiplication of experiments, and the systematic accumulation of knowledge and learning over time. As a result, the formalistic company becomes more dense, interactive and adaptable. The quality dynamic prepares it for the next and even greater challenge: flexibility. This represents an even more difficult challenge, since it requires a formidable combination of quality, innovation and faster reaction to customers' demands, in other words a combination of discipline and creativity.

Enough said! Quality is a little inspiration and a lot of perspiration. What really counts is action. The map has been plotted, and only practice will teach each of us the particular road we must follow. Every company must invent its own route, guided by the concepts and milestones we have endeavoured to set out but also taking into account its individual culture and background. Have a good journey!

BIBLIOGRAPHY

1. General Bibliography (books)

Abernathy, W. J., Clark, K. B., and Kantrow, A. M. (1983), *Industrial Renaissance: Producing a competitive future for America*, New York: Basic Books.

Bernard, C. (1865, rpt 1966), *Introduction à la médecine expérimentale*, Bordas, France.

Bolwijn, P. T., Boorsma, J., van Breukelen, Q., Brinkman, S., and Kumpe, T. (1986), *Flexible Manufacturing, Integrating Technological and Social Innovation*, Amsterdam: Elsevier.

Chase, R. B., and Aquilano, N. J. (1985), *Production and Operations Management*, 4th edition, Homewood, IL: Richard D. Irwin.

Cyert, R. M., and March, J. G. (1963), *A Behavioral Theory of the Firm*, Englewood Cliffs, NJ: Prentice Hall.

Foulkes, F. K. (1980), *Personnel Policies in Large Non-union Companies*, Englewood Cliffs, NJ: Prentice Hall.

Goldratt, E. M., and Cox, J. (1984), *The Goal: Excellence in manufacturing*, New York: North River Press.

Hackman, J. R., and Oldham G. R. (1980), *Work Redesign*, Boston, MA: Addison Wesley.

Hall, E. T. (1959), *The Silent Language*, New York: Doubleday.

Hall, E. T. (1976), *Beyond Culture*, New York: Doubleday.

Hayes, R. H., and Wheelwright, S. C. (1984), *Restoring our Competitive Edge: Competing through manufacturing*, New York: John Wiley.

Hayes, R. H., Wheelwright, S. C., and Clark, K. B. (1988), *Dynamic Manufacturing*, New York: Free Press.

March, J., and Simon, H. (1958), *Organizations*, New York: John Wiley.

Peters, T. (1988), *Thriving on Chaos: Handbook for a management revolution*, New York: Alfred A. Knopf.

Peters, T. J. and Austin, N. (1985), *A Passion for Excellence*, New York: Random House.

Peters, T. J., and Waterman R. H. (1982), *In Search of Excellence*, New York: Harper & Row.

Porter, M. E. (1985), *Competitive Advantage*, New York: The Free Press.

Schein, E. (1988), *Organizational Culture and Leadership*, CA: Jossey Bass.

Schmenner, R. W. (1984), *Production/Operations Management: Concepts and situations*, 2nd edition, Chicago: Science Research Associates.

Schonberger, R. J. (1982), *Japanese Manufacturing Techniques: Nine hidden lessons in simplicity*, New York: Free Press.

Schonberger, R. J. (1986), *World Class Manufacturing: The lessons of simplicity applied*, New York: Free Press.

Shingo, S. (1981), *Study of Toyota Production Systems*, Japan Management Association, distributed by Productivity Inc., P.O. Box 814, Cambridge, MA 02238.

Simon, H. (1957), *Administrative Behaviour*, London: Macmillan.

Skinner, W. (1978), *Manufacturing in the Corporate Strategy*, New York: John Wiley.

Skinner, W. (1985), *Manuracturing: The formidable competitive weapon*, New York: John Wiley.

Suzaki, K. (1987), *The New Manufacturing Challenge: Techniques for continuous improvement*, New York: Free Press, London: Collier MacMillan Publishers.

2. Management of Services (books)

Albrecht, K., and Zemke, R. (1985), *Service America*, Homewood, IL: Dow Jones-Irwin.

Carlzon, J. (1986), *Renversons la pyramide*, Paris: Interéditions.

Carlzon, J. (1987), *Moments of Truth*, Cambridge, MA: Ballinger Publishing.

Collier, D. A. (1987), *Service Management: Operating decisions*, Englewood Cliffs, NJ: Prentice Hall.

Collier, D. A. (1985), *Service Management: The automation of services*, Reston, VA: Reston Publishing Company.

Eiglier, P., and Langeard, E. (1987), *Servuction: Le marketing des services*, Paris: McGraw-Hill.

Fitzsimmons, J. A., and Sullivan, R. S. (1982), *Service Operations Management*, New York: McGraw-Hill.

Heskett, J. L. (1986), *Managing in the Service Economy*, Boston, MA: Harvard Business School Press.

Lovelock, C. H. (1988), *Managing Services: Marketing, operations and human resources*, Englewood Cliffs, NJ: Prentice Hall.

Mills, P. K. (1986), *Managing Service Industries: Organizational practices in a post-industrial economy*, Cambridge, MA: Ballinger Publishing.

Moores, B. (1986), *Are They Being Served? Quality consciousness in service industries*, Oxford: Philip Allan.

Normann, R. (1984), *Service Management: Strategy and leadership in service businesses*, New York: John Wiley.

Parasuraman, A., Zeithaml, V., and Leonard, L. B. (1986), *Servqual: A multiple-item scale for measuring customer perceptions of service quality*, Cambridge, MA: Marketing Science Institute Research Program.

Rajan, A. (1987), *Services – The second industrial revolution?* Institute of Manpower Studies. London: Butterworth.

Riddle, D. I. (1986), *Service-Led Growth*, New York: Praeger.

Sasser, W. E., Olsen, R. P., and Wyckoff, D. D. (1982), *Management of Service Operations. Text, Cases and Readings*, Boston, MA: Allyn and Bacon.

Voss, C. A., Armistead, D. G., Johnston, R., and Morris, B. (1985), *Operations Management in Service Industries and the Public Sector*, Chichester: John Wiley.

Wegner, O. (1987), *Service Economies in Europe: Opportunities for growth*, London: Pinter Publishing.

3. Quality Management (books)

Barker, T. B. (1985), *Quality by Experimental Design*, New York: Marcel Dekker.

Barra, R. (1983), *Putting Quality Circles to Work*, New York: McGraw-Hill.

Crosby, P. B. (1980), *Quality is Free*, New York: New American Library.

Crosby, P. B. (1984), *Quality Without Tears*, New York: McGraw-Hill.

Dale B., and Plunkett, G. (1989), *Managing Quality*, London: Philip Allan.

Delbecq, Van de Ven A. H., and Gustafson, D. H. (1975), *Group Techniques for Program Planning: A guide to nominal group and Delphi processes*, Glenview, IL: Scott, Foresman.

Deming, W. E. (1982), *Quality, Productivity and Competitive Position*, Cambridge, MA: MIT Press.

Deming, W. E. (1986), *Out of the Crisis*, Boston, MA: MIT Center for Advanced Engineering Study.

Feigenbaum, A. V. (1961, 1963), *Total Quality Control*. New York: McGraw-Hill.

Fine, C. H., and Bridge, D. H. (1984), *Managing Quality Improvement*, WP 1607–84, Boston, MA: Sloan School of Management, MIT.

Garvin, D. A. (1988), *Managing Quality – the strategic and competitive edge*, New York: Free Press.

Grant, E. L., and Leavenworth, R. (1980), *Statistical Quality Control*, New York: McGraw-Hill.

Groocock, J. M. (1986), *The Chain of Quality–Market dominance through product superiority*, New York: John Wiley.

Gusapari, J. (1985), *I Know It When I See It: Modern fable about quality*, New York: American Management Association.

Harrington, H. J. (1987), *The Improvement Process: How American leading companies improve quality*, New York: McGraw-Hill.

Imai, M. (1986), *Kaizen – The key to Japan's competitive success*, New York: Random House Business Division.

Ingle, S. (1982), *Quality Circles Master Guide: Increasing productivity with people power*, Englewood Cliffs, NJ: Prentice Hall.

Ishikawa, K. (1985), *What is Total Quality Control? The Japanese Way*, Englewood Cliffs, NJ: Prentice Hall.

Jacoby, J., and Olson, J. C. (1985), *Perceived Quality – How consumers view stores and merchandise*, Lexington, MA: Lexington Books.

Juran, J. M. (1964), *Managerial Breakthrough*, New York: McGraw-Hill.

Juran, J. M. (1974), *Quality Control Handbook*, New York: McGraw-Hill.

Juran, J. M., and Gryna, F. M. (1980), *Quality Planning and Analysis*, New York: McGraw-Hill.

Martin, W. B. (1986), *Quality Service: The restaurant manager's bible*. Ithaca, NY: Cornell University.

McCormick, C. (1978), *The Statistical Control of Process Quality*, Texas: Continental Carbon Company.

Oakland, J. S. (1989), *Total Quality Management*, Oxford: Heinemann.

Oakland, J. S., and Followell, R. F. (1986; first publication) *Statistical Process Control*, Oxford: Heinemann Newnes, reprinted 1986, 1987, 1989.

Ott, E. R. (1975), *Process Quality Control: Troubleshooting and interpretation of data*, Tokyo: McGraw-Hill Kogakusha.

Ould, M. A. (1990), *Strategies for Software Engineering: The management of risk and quality*, New York: John Wiley.

Perrow, C. (1984), *Normal Accidents*, New York: Basic Books.

Price, F. (1984), *Right First Time*, Aldershot: Wildwood House.

Robson, M. (1984), *Quality Circles in Action*, Aldershot: Gower.

Rosander, A. C. (1985), *Applications of Quality Control in the Service Industries*, New York: Marcel Dekker, ASQC Quality Press.

Ross, J. E., and Ross, W. (1982), *Japanese Quality Circles and Productivity*, Reston, VA: Reston Publishing.

Shetty, Y. K., and Buehler, V. M. (1987), *Quality, Productivity and Innovation Strategies for Gaining Competitive Advantage*, Amsterdam: Elsevier Science Publishing.

Shingo, S. (1986), *Zero Quality Control: Source inspection and the poka-yoke system*, Cambridge, MA: Productivity Press.

Shores, R. A. (1988), *Survival of the Fittest – Total quality control and management evolution*, ASQC Quality Press, American Society for Quality Control, 310 West Wisconsin Avenue, Milwaukee, Wisconsin 53203.

Sinha, M. N., and Willborn, W. W. O. (1985), *The Management of Quality Assurance*, New York: John Wiley.

Taguchi, G. (1981), *On-line Quality Control during Production*, Japanese Standards Association, 1-24, Akasaka 4-chome Minato-ku, Tokyo, 107, Japan.

Taguchi, G., and Wu, Y. (1985), *Introduction to Off-Line Quality Control*, Central Japan Quality Control Association, 2nd Toyota Bldg 3F, 4-10-27 Meieki Nakamura-ku Nagaya, Japan.

Thompson, P. C. (1982), *Quality Circles: How to make them work in America*, New York: Amalcom.

Townsend, P. L., and Gebhardt, J. E. (1986), *Commit to Quality*, New York: John Wiley.

4. Articles on Services

Berry, L. L. (1981), 'The employee as a customer', *The Journal of Retail Banking*, vol. 3, no. 1.

Chase, R. B. (1978), 'Where does the customer fit in a service operation?', *Harvard Business Review*, vol. 56, no. 4, Nov.–Dec., pp. 137–42.

Hart, C., Heskett, I. and Sasser, W., 'The profitable art of service recovery', *Harvard Business Review*, July–Aug. 1990.

Hostage, G. M. (1975), 'Quality control in a service business', *Harvard Business Review*, vol. 53, no. 4, July–Aug., pp. 98–106.

Levitt, T. (1972), 'Production-line approach to service', *Harvard Business Review*, vol. 50, no. 5, Sept.–Oct., pp. 41–52.

Levitt, T. (1976), 'The industrialization of service', *Harvard Business Review*, Sept.–Oct., pp. 63–74.

Matteis, R. J. (1979), 'The new back office focuses on customer service', *Harvard Business Review*, vol. 57, no. 2, March–April, pp. 146–59.

Morris, B., and Johnston, R. (1987), 'Dealing with inherent variability – the difference between service and manufacturing explained', *The International Journal of Operations and Production Management*, vol. 7, no. 4, pp. 13–22.

Quinn, J. B., and Gagnon, C. E. (1986), 'Will services follow manufacturing into decline', *Harvard Business Review*, vol. 64, no. 6, Nov.–Dec., pp. 95–103.

Shostack, G. L., 'How to design a service', *European Journal of Marketing*, vol. 16, no. 1, pp. 49–63.

Teboul, J. (1988), 'De-industrialize service for quality', *Strategy, Quality and Resource Management in the Service Sector*, vol. 8, no. 3, pp. 39–44.

Wyckoff, D. D. (1984), 'New tools for achieving service quality', *The Cornell HRA Quarterly*, Nov., pp. 78–91.

5. Articles on Quality

Campanella, J., and Corcoran, F. J. (1983), 'Principles of quality costs', *Quality Progress*, vol. 16, no. 4, pp. 16–22.

Clausing, D. P. (1987), 'Improved total development process: changing the ten cash drains into a cash flow', American Supplier Institute, *Quality Function Deployment*, section 6.

Cole, R. E. (1980), 'Learning from the Japanese: prospects and pitfalls', *Management Review*, Sept., pp. 22–42.

Cole, R. E. (1981), 'The Japanese lesson in quality', *Technology Review*, Spring, pp. 29–40.

Dale, B. G., and Hayward, S. G. (1985), 'Quality circle failure and how to avoid it', *European Management Journal*, vol. 3, no. 2, pp. 103–11.

Dale, B. G., and Lees, J. (1987), 'Quality circles: from introduction to integration', *Long Range Planning*, vol. 20, no. 1, pp. 78–83.

Dearborn, D. C., and Simon, H. A. (1958), 'Selective perception', *Sociometry*, vol. 21, pp. 140–4.

Doran, P. (1985), 'A total quality improvement programme', *International Journal of Quality and Reliability Management*, vol. 2, no. 3.

Eureka, W. E. (1987), 'Quality function deployment in the context of Taguchi methods', American Supplier Institute, *Quality Function Deployment*, section III.

Fukuhara, A. (1987), 'QFD and the other tools: excerpts from the Toyota rust QFD study', presented by Mr W. E. Eureka, American Supplier Institute, *Quality Function Deployment*, section V.

Garvin, D. A. (1983), 'Quality on the line', *Harvard Business Review*, Sept.–Oct., pp. 64–75.

Garvin, D. A. (1987), 'Competing on the eight dimensions of quality', *Harvard Business Review*, Nov.–Dec., pp. 101–9.

Gerstner, E. (1985), 'Do higher prices signal higher quality?', *Journal of Marketing Research*, vol. 32, May, pp. 209–15.

Hagan, J. T. (1984), 'The management of quality: preparing for a competitive future', *Quality Progress*, December, pp. 21–5.

Hart, C., and Casserly, G. (1985), 'Quality: a brand-new, time-tested strategy', *The Cornell HRA Quarterly*, November, pp. 52–62.

Hauser, J., and Clausing, D. (1988), 'The house of quality', *Harvard Business Review*, May–June, pp. 63–73.

Hayes, R. and Wheelwright, S. (1979), 'Link manufacturing process and product life cycles', *Harvard Business Review*, Jan–Feb.

Hertzberg, F. (1967, 1987), 'One more time, how do you motivate employees', *Harvard Business Review*, Sept.–Oct., pp. 109–20.

Juran, J. M. (1986), *The Quality Trilogy: A universal approach to managing for quality*, Juran Publication Institute, 88 Danbury Rd, CT 06897-4409.

Kearns, D. T. (1989), 'Payment in kind', *Quality Progress*, April, pp. 16–20.

Kobayashi, Y. (1981), 'Quality control in Japan: the case of Fuji Xerox', *Institute of Comparative Culture Business Series*, bulletin No. 81, Sophia University, Tokyo.

Lawler III, E. E., and Mohrman, S. A. (1985), 'Quality circles after the fad', *Harvard Business Review*, Jan.–Feb., pp. 65–71.

Lascelles, D. M., and Dale, B. G. (1989), 'Quality improvement: what is the motivation?', *Proc. Inst. Mech. Eng.*, vol. 203, pp. 43–50.

Lascelles, D. M., and Dale, B. G. (1989), 'The key issues of a quality improvement process', *Int. J. Prod. Res.*, vol. 27, pp. 1–13.

Lascelles, D. M., and Dale, B. G. (1989), 'The national quality campaign: a study of its impact on industry', *Proc. Inst. Mech. Eng.*, vol. 203, pp. 201–9.

McDonnell, S. N. (1985), 'Implementing quality improvement at McDonnell Douglas', Juran report IMPRO-85, Juran Institute.

de Meyer, A., Miller, J., Nakane, J., Ferdows, K. (1989), 'Flexibility: the next competitive battle', *Strategic Management Journal*, vol. 10, pp. 135–44.

Miller J. G., and Vollmann, T. E. (1985), 'The hidden factory', *Harvard Business Review*, Sept.–Oct., pp. 142–50.

Morrell, N. E. (1987), *Quality Function Deployment*, American Supplier Institute, Michigan.

Kenichi, O. (1983), 'The "strategic triangle" and business unit strategy', *The McKinsey Quarterly*, Winter, pp. 9–23.

Onnias, A. (1985), *The Quality Blue Book*, Juran report IMPRO-85, Juran Institute.

Ossela, Denis A. (1981), 'The application of Japanese productivity and quality control methods to an American workforce', *Manufacturing Productivity Frontiers*, May, pp. 1–8.

Perry, G. R. (1986), 'Putting the quality function deployment concept to work', Allied-Signal Automotive Sector 25th Annual Fall Conference, Dearborn, Michigan, 15 October.

Phillips, L. W., Hang, D. R., and Buzzell, D. R. (1983), 'Product quality, cost position and business performance: a test of some key hypotheses', *Journal of Marketing*, vol. 47, pp. 26–43.

Ross, J. E., and Krishna, Y. (1985), 'Making quality a fundamental part of strategy', *Long Range Planning*, vol. 18, no. 1, pp. 53–8.

Shea, G. P. (1986), 'Quality circles: the danger of bottled change', *Sloan Management Review*, Spring, pp. 33–46.

Sullivan, L. P. (1984), 'Reducing variability: a new approach to quality', *Quality Progress*, July, pp. 15–21.

Sullivan, L. P. (1986), 'The seven stages in company-wide quality control', *Quality Progress*, May, pp. 77–83.

Sullivan, L. P. (1986), 'Quality function deployment', *Quality Progress*, June, pp. 39–50.

Taguchi, G., and Clausing, D. (1988), 'Robust quality', *Harvard Business Review*, Jan.–Feb., pp. 65–75.

Tribus, M. (1984), 'Reducing Deming's 14 points to practice', Massachusetts Institute of Technology, June.

Tribus, M., and Yoshikazu, T. (1984), 'Creating the quality company', Massachusetts Institute of Technology.

Wood. R., Hull, F., and Azumi, K. (1983), 'Evaluating quality circles: the American application', *California Management Review*, vol. 26, no. 1, Fall, pp. 37–53.

6. Cases and Notes

'Benihana of Tokyo' (1972), Harvard Business School
case no. 9-673-057, Boston, MA: HBS Case Services, Harvard Business School.

BIBLIOGRAPHY

'Mickey Mouse Marketing' (1986), Harvard Business School
    notes nos 8-687-067 and 8-687-068, Boston, MA: HBS Case Services, Harvard Business
    School.
'Paul Revere Insurance Company (B)' (1981), Harvard Business School
    case no. 9-687-033, Boston, MA: HBS Case Services, Harvard Business School.
'The SPEA Case (A)' (1986), INSEAD-CEDEP, Fontainebleau: INSEAD Case Services.
'Steinway and Sons' (1981), Harvard Business School
    case no. 9-682-025, Boston, MA: HBS Case Services, Harvard Business School.

INDEX